EASY PICKINGS
ACOUSTIC HITS

WISE PUBLICATIONS
part of The Music Sales Group
London / New York / Paris / Sydney / Copenhagen / Berlin / Madrid / Tokyo

GW00385512

Published by
WISE PUBLICATIONS
14-15 Berners Street, London W1T 3LJ, UK.

Exclusive Distributors:
MUSIC SALES LIMITED
Distribution Centre, Newmarket Road,
Bury St Edmunds, Suffolk IP33 3YB, UK.
MUSIC SALES PTY LIMITED
Music Sales Pty Limited
20 Resolution Drive, Caringbah, NSW 2229, Australia.

Order No. AM991749
ISBN 978-1-84772-269-0
This book © Copyright 2008 Wise Publications,
a division of Music Sales Limited.

Music edited by Tom Farncombe
Music arranged by David Weston
Music processed by Paul Ewers Music Design
Photos courtesy LFI
Cover illustration courtesy iStockphoto
Printed in the EU

Your Guarantee of Quality
As publishers, we strive to produce every book to the
highest commercial standards. This book has been carefully
designed to minimise awkward page turns and to make
playing from it a real pleasure. Particular care has been
given to specifying acid-free, neutral-sized paper made
from pulps which have not been elemental chlorine
bleached. This pulp is from farmed sustainable forests and
was produced with special regard for the environment.
Throughout, the printing and binding have been planned
to ensure a sturdy, attractive publication which should give
years of enjoyment. If your copy fails to meet our high
standards, please inform us and we will gladly replace it.

www.musicsales.com

WELCOME TO EASY PICKINGS™!

EASY PICKINGS is the new way to play classic songs in the finger picking style. The music in this book doesn't use standard notation. Instead, a simple system shows the guitar strings.

Chord boxes show you where to place your fingers with your fretting hand; crosses on the strings show you the pattern to pick the strings. That's all there is to it!

All the songs in this book have been specially arranged in the EASY PICKINGS format to make them as easy as possible. The first few songs have only a few chords, and simple picking patterns; later in the book the songs have more chords and a greater variety of finger picking styles. Some of the songs have been arranged in a different key from the original recording. Where this is the case, you'll need a capo, at the fret indicated at the top of the song, to play along.

The pictures below show you all you need to know!

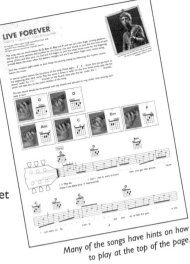

Many of the songs have hints on how to play at the top of the page.

CHORD BOXES

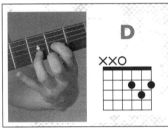

*Chord box for a **D** chord.*

Chord boxes are diagrams of the guitar neck viewed head upwards, face on.
They show where to place your fingers to play each chord. Each time you see a new chord box, change to the new chord.

The top line is the nut, the others are the frets. The vertical lines are the strings, starting from E (or 6th) on the left to E (or 1st) on the right.

The black dots indicate where to place your fingers. Strings marked with an O are played open, not fretted; strings marked with an X should not be played. You won't always pick every note of every chord shape that you finger, but it is important to hold each chord in full to learn properly.

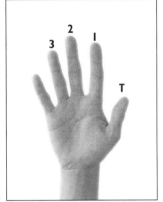

FINGER PICKING

At the start of each song, you'll see the guitar headstock and the strings of the guitar, viewed as if you were playing. The crosses on the strings show each note to be picked with your picking hand.

Usually, you'll play the first note of each group of four with your thumb (**T**), and the other notes with your 1st (**1**), 2nd (**2**) and 3rd (**3**) fingers. This is shown above some of the patterns as a guide. Follow these fingerings and you'll be playing all the finger picking patterns in this book in no time!

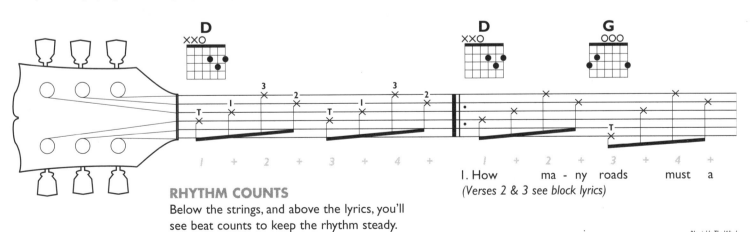

RHYTHM COUNTS

Below the strings, and above the lyrics, you'll see beat counts to keep the rhythm steady.
Each number (or +) is a note to pick.

1. How ma-ny roads must a
(Verses 2 & 3 see block lyrics)

LIVE FOREVER
WORDS & MUSIC BY NOEL GALLAGHER

This song uses six chord shapes: **G**, **D**, **Am**, **C**, **Em** and **F**, and has two main finger picking patterns — one for the verse sections, and another for the chorus. Use your thumb to pick the first note of each group of four, and then your 1st, 2nd and 3rd fingers to pick the other three. Look for the fingerings printed above the music when the pattern changes, and you'll see which finger picks which string.

Each bar contains eight notes to pick. Keep the picking steady by following the rhythm counts below the music.

A special system shows the structure of the song. These signs — ‖: :‖ — show that you go back to the beginning after each verse. Play the verse 4 times in total. On the first three times, play the bar shown under the ⌐1, 2, 3.⌐ bracket; on the fourth time, play the bar under the ⌐4.⌐ bracket, which will take you to the outro section of the song.

The last chord should be strummed with the thumb and allowed to ring, rather than picking each note in turn.

Live Forever was the first Oasis song to reach the UK top ten (guitarist and songwriter Noel Gallagher pictured above).

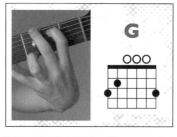

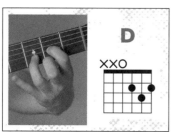

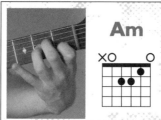

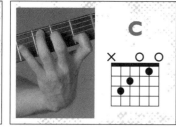

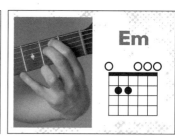

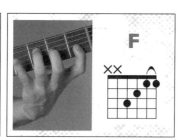

Verse

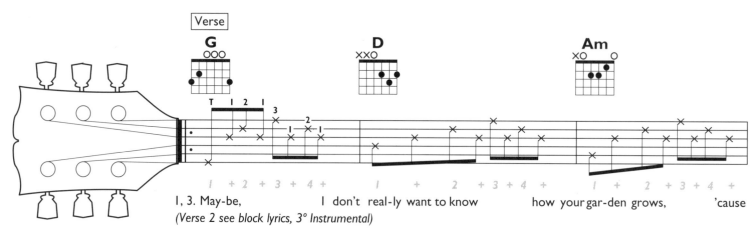

1, 3. May-be, I don't real-ly want to know how your gar-den grows, 'cause
(Verse 2 see block lyrics, 3° Instrumental)

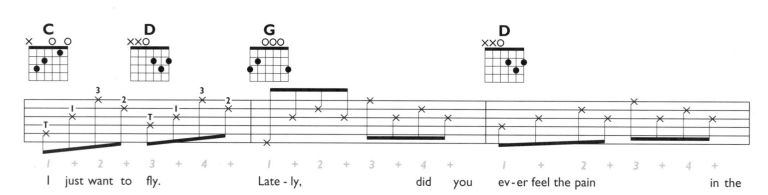

I just want to fly. Late - ly, did you ev - er feel the pain in the

4

Verse 2:
I said maybe, I don't really want to know,
How your garden grows, I just want to fly.
Lately, did you ever feel the pain,
In the morning rain, as it soaks you to the bone.

Maybe I will never be, all the things I want to be,
But now is not the time to cry, now's the time to find out why.
I think you're the same as me, we see things they'll never see,
You and I are going to live forever.

WONDERFUL TONIGHT
WORDS & MUSIC BY ERIC CLAPTON

This ballad uses five chords: **G**, **D**, **C**, **Em**, and **D/F#** (see photo below). This last chord is used in this song to create a smooth bass line linking the chords **G** and **Em**.

Follow the fingerings for each picking pattern and the crosses on the strings carefully. For the progression **G** to **D/F#** to **Em**, you pick strings 4, 3 and 2 with your fingers, instead of strings 3, 2 and 1. Practise this slowly to start with, until you can smoothly shift between each hand position.

Special symbols are used here to show the structure of the song. Start with the intro, which repeats, as shown by the ‖: :‖ signs. Then play verse 1, which ends with the music shown under the ⌐1.⎯; go back to the beginning of the verse for verse 2, and this time play the ⌐2.⎯ to go to the bridge section. After the bridge, you'll see the instruction ***Go back to*** 𝄋. This takes you to the 𝄋 symbol, back at the beginning of the verse. On this third time through, look for the ***Go to*** ⊕ sign, and jump to the ⊕ section on page 8 to finish the song.

This song featured on Eric Clapton's 1977 album Slowhand.

D/F#

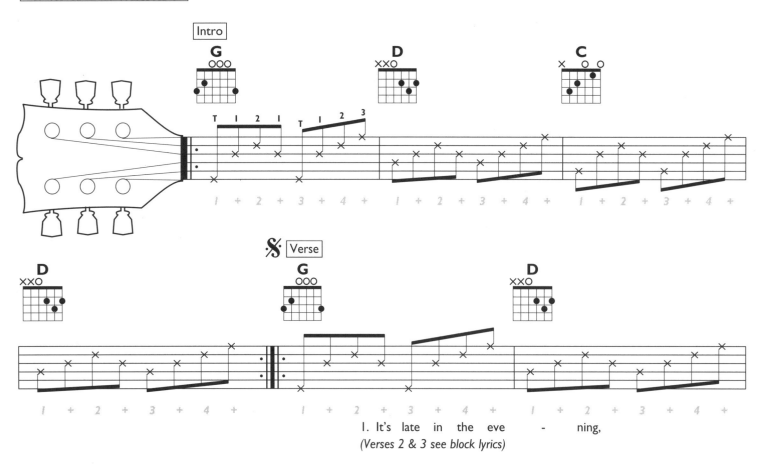

1. It's late in the eve - ning,
(Verses 2 & 3 see block lyrics)

she's wonder-ing what clothes to wear. She puts on her make-

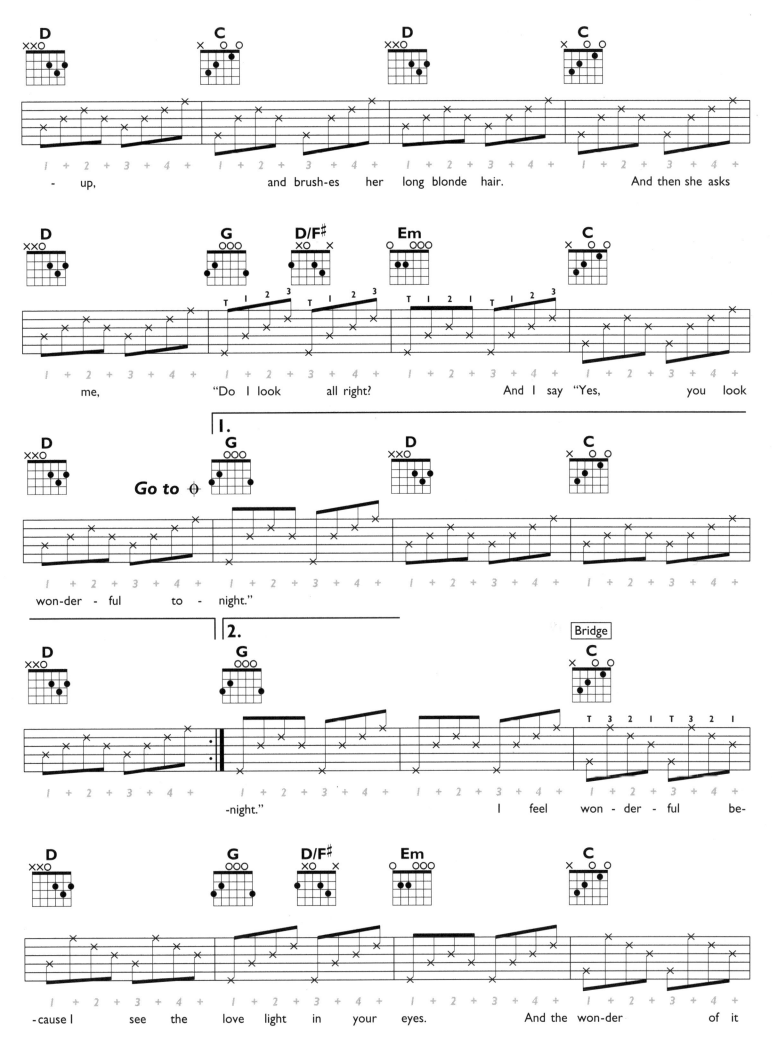

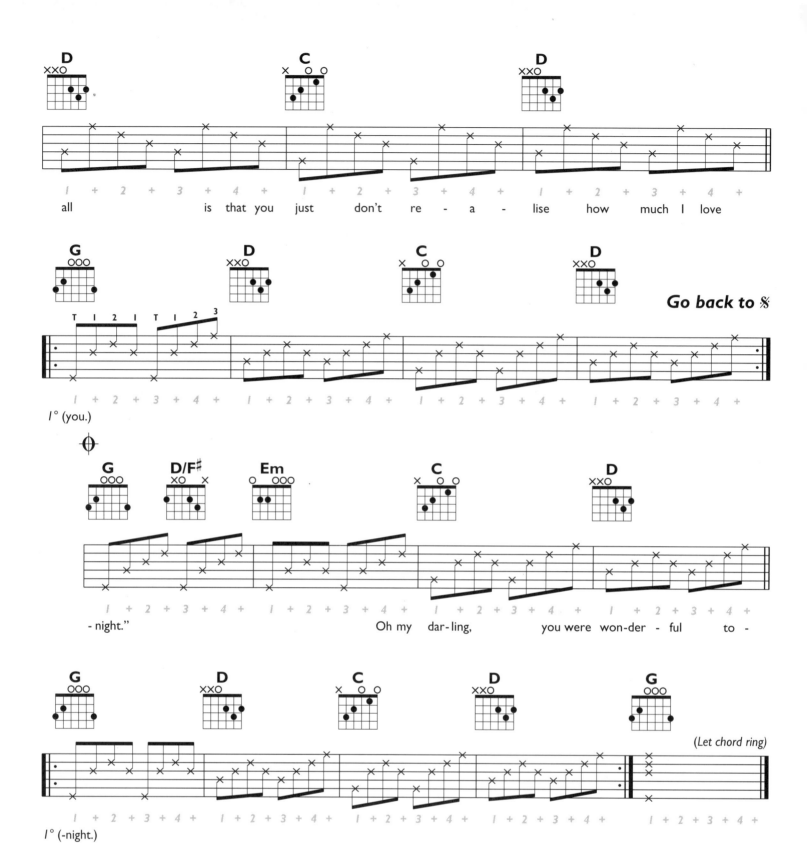

Verse 2:
We go to a party and everyone turns to see
This beautiful lady that's walking around with me.
And then she asks me, "Do you feel all right?"
And I say, "Yes, I feel wonderful tonight."

Verse 3:
It's time to go home now and I've got an aching head,
So I give her the car keys and she helps me to bed.
And then I tell her, as I turn out the light,
I say, "My darling, you were wonderful tonight.
Oh my darling, you were wonderful tonight."

NO WOMAN, NO CRY

WORDS & MUSIC BY VINCENT FORD

The chord **C/B** is used in this song to create a smooth bass line between the chords **C** and **Am**. All the sections of the song are based on the chords from the intro, using one picking pattern, so once you have mastered the first four bars, you will be able to play the entire song!

Look for the repeat symbols – 𝄆 𝄇 𝄋 ⊕ – that show the song structure.

To match the key of the original recording, you'll need a capo, fixed at the first fret.

The most famous version of this song is on Bob Marley's 1975 Live! Album.

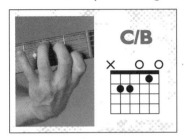

CAPO: 1ST FRET

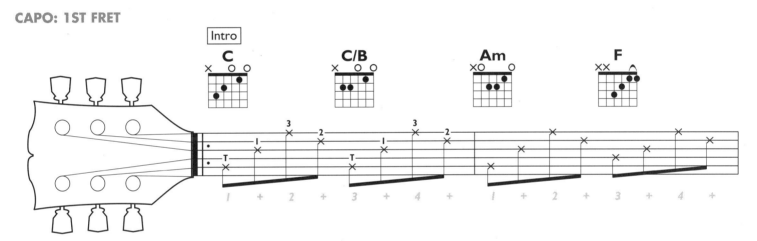

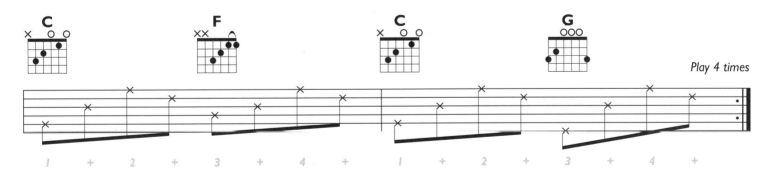

Play 4 times

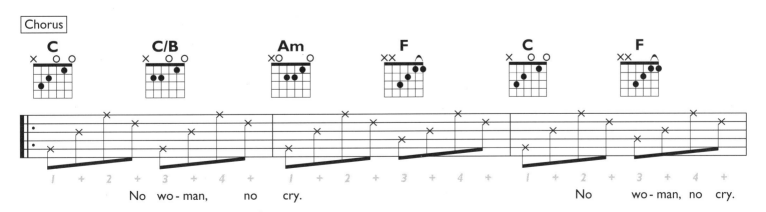

No wo-man, no cry.   No wo-man, no cry.

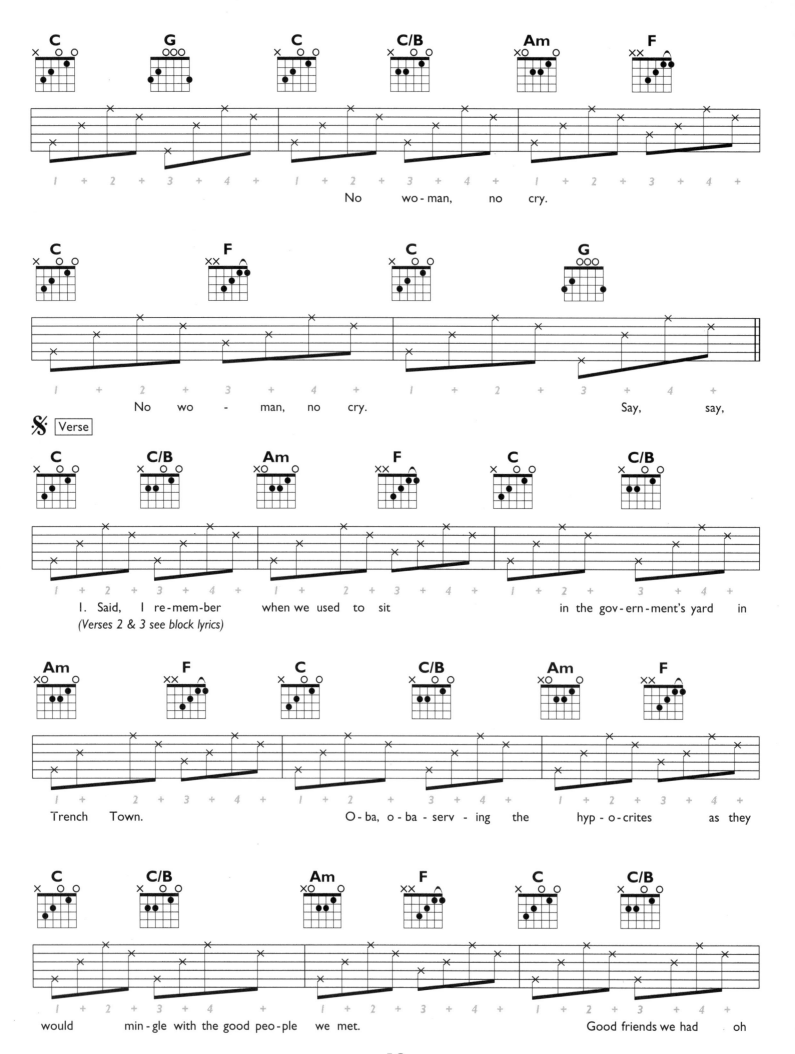

No wo-man, no cry.

No wo - man, no cry. Say, say,

𝄋 Verse

1. Said, I re-mem-ber when we used to sit in the gov-ern-ment's yard in
(Verses 2 & 3 see block lyrics)

Trench Town. O-ba, o-ba-serv - ing the hyp-o-crites as they

would min - gle with the good peo-ple we met. Good friends we had oh

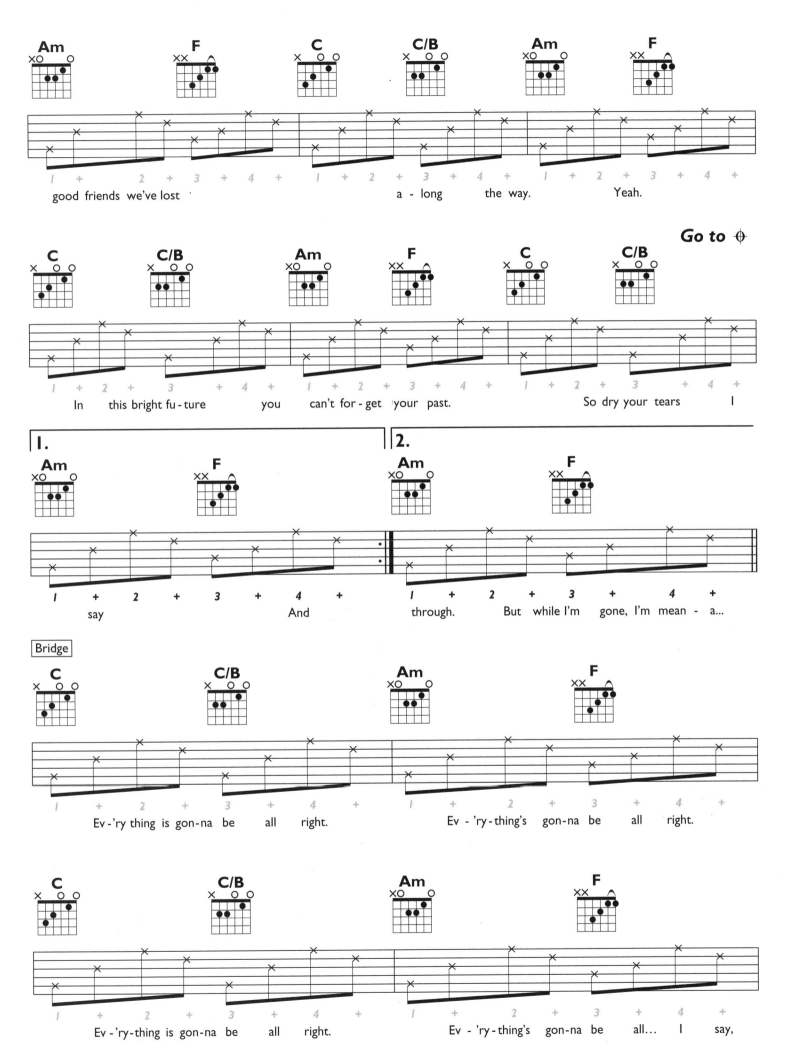

good friends we've lost a - long the way. Yeah.

Go to ⊕

In this bright fu - ture you can't for - get your past. So dry your tears I

1. say And

2. through. But while I'm gone, I'm mean - a...

Bridge

Ev -'ry thing is gon-na be all right. Ev -'ry-thing's gon-na be all right.

Ev -'ry-thing is gon-na be all right. Ev -'ry-thing's gon-na be all... I say,

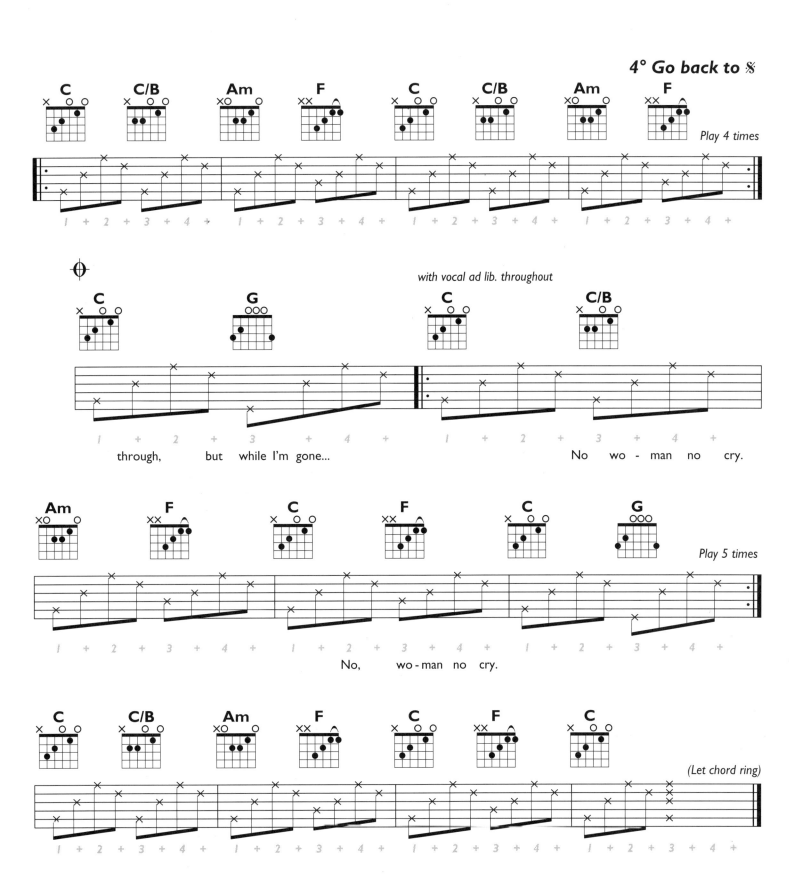

Verse 2:
I remember when-a we used to sit
In the government yard in Trenchtown.
And then Georgie would make a fire light,
As it was logwood burning through the night.

Verse 3:
Then we would cook cornmeal porridge,
Of which I'll share with you
My feet is my only carriage,
So I've got to push on through.
But while I'm gone, I mean:

HEY, THAT'S NO WAY TO SAY GOODBYE

WORDS & MUSIC BY LEONARD COHEN

The intro section for this song, and the last bar of each verse, uses a picking pattern where two strings are picked at once. This is shown in the photo below.

Follow the rhythm counts carefully – the last bar has five counts, instead of four.

This song was first released on Leonard Cohen's debut album, Songs from Leonard Cohen, in 1968.

Picking the 4th and 2nd strings together.

CAPO: 3RD FRET

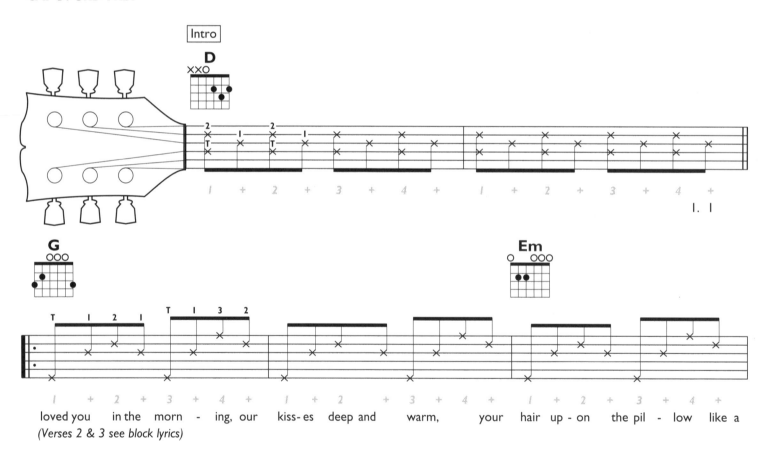

loved you   in the morn - ing, our kiss - es deep and   warm,   your   hair up - on   the pil - low   like a
(Verses 2 & 3 see block lyrics)

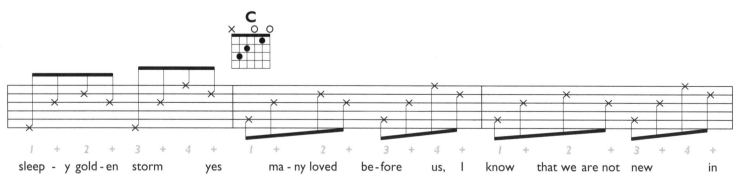

sleep - y gold - en   storm   yes   ma - ny loved   be - fore   us, I   know   that we are not new   in

14

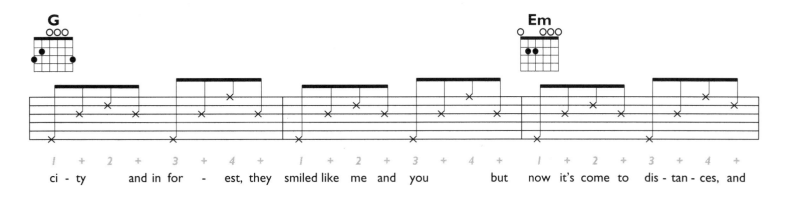

ci - ty   and in for - est, they smiled like me and you   but   now it's come to dis - tan - ces, and

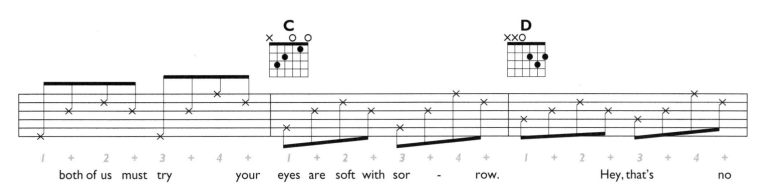

both of us must try   your eyes are soft with sor - row.   Hey, that's   no

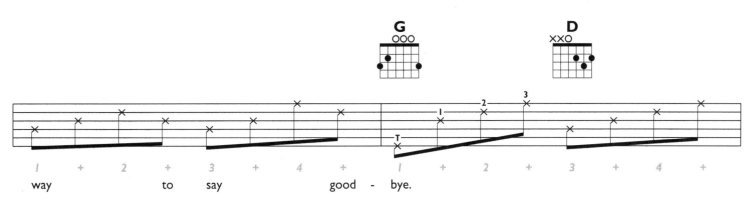

way   to say   good - bye.

(3rd time begin to fade)   *Play 3 times*

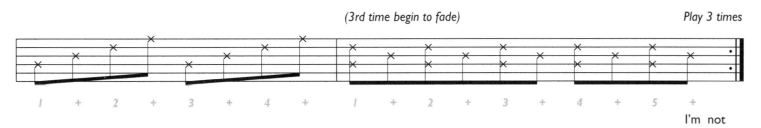

I'm not

Verse 2:
I'm not looking for another
As I wander in my time,
Walk me to the corner
Our steps will always rhyme,
You know my love goes with you
As your love stays with me,
It's just the way it changes
Like the shoreline and the sea,
But let's not talk of love or chains
And things we can't untie,
Your eyes are soft with sorrow,
Hey, that's no way to say goodbye.

Verse 3:
I loved you in the morning
Our kisses deep and warm,
Your head upon the pillow
Like a sleepy golden storm.
Yes, many loved before us
I know that we are not new,
In city and in forest
They smiled like me and you,
But let's not talk of love or chains
And things we can't untie,
Your eyes are soft with sorrow,
Hey, that's no way to say goodbye.

LEAN ON ME

WORDS AND MUSIC BY BILL WITHERS

This song was first released on the 1972 Bill Withers album Still Bill.

The ⊕ section of this song alternates between **C** and **F/C**, shown in the photo below. After the first bar of this section, the symbol ∕. is used. This is shorthand to show that the pattern repeats exactly for these bars. This symbol is also used in the bridge section.

Observe the crosses on the strings carefully for each chord shape. You won't always be picking the lowest note of the chord (for instance, for the **G** chord in the second bar of the second line).

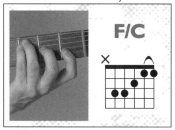

CAPO: 3RD FRET

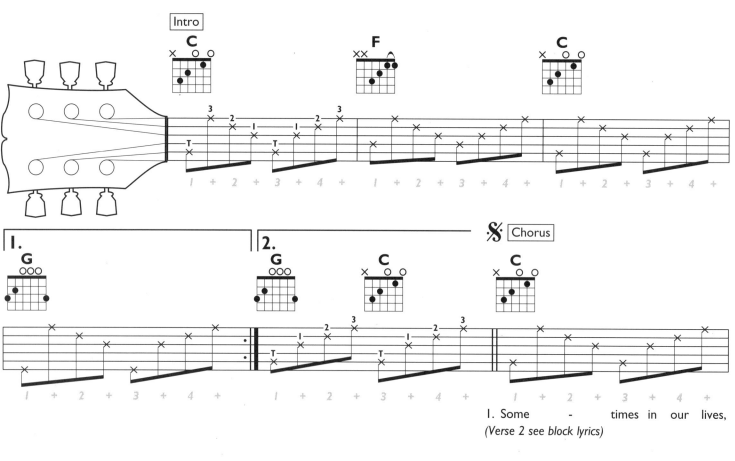

1. Some - times in our lives,
(Verse 2 see block lyrics)

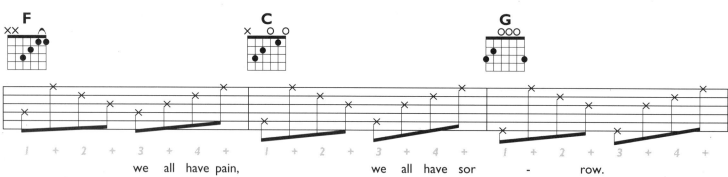

we all have pain,   we all have sor - row.

16

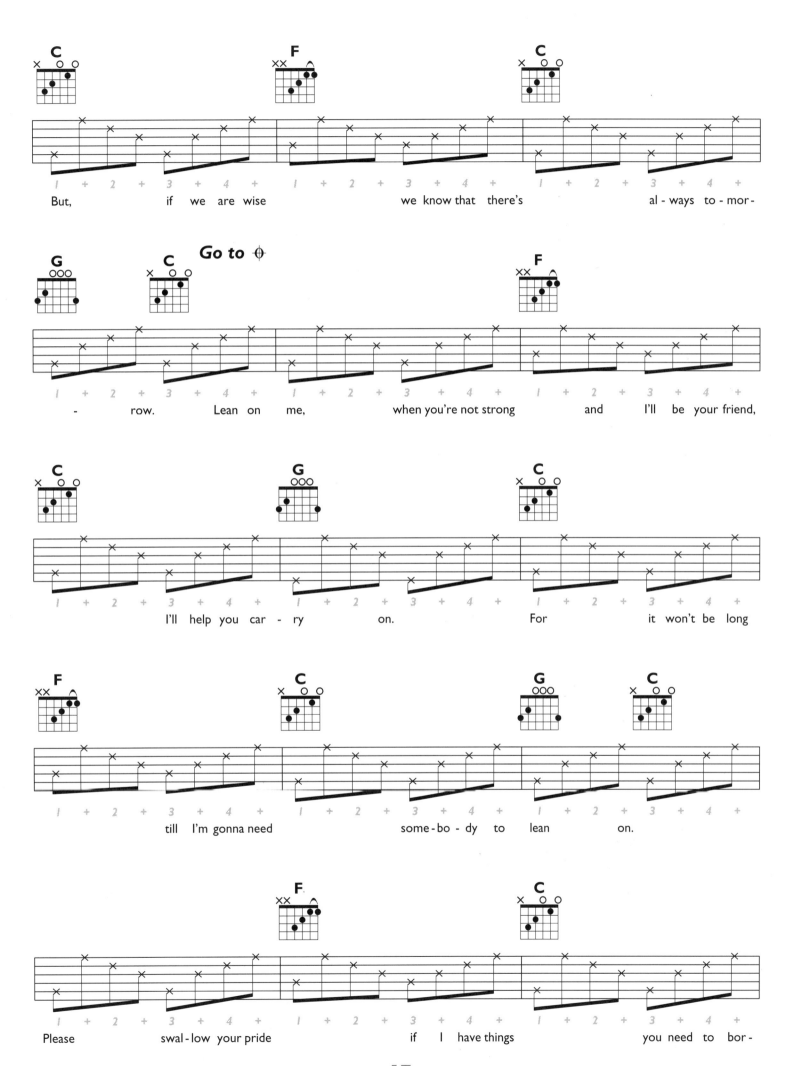

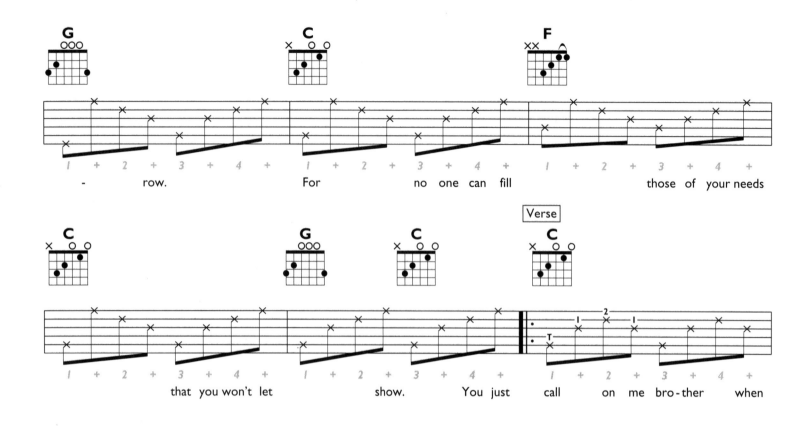

- row.   For   no one can fill   those of your needs

that you won't let   show.   You just   call   on me bro-ther   when

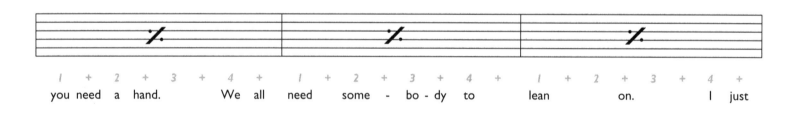

you need a hand.   We all   need   some - bo - dy to   lean   on.   I just

might   have a prob-lem   that   you'll un - der-stand.   We all   need   some - bo - dy to

2° Go back to 𝄋

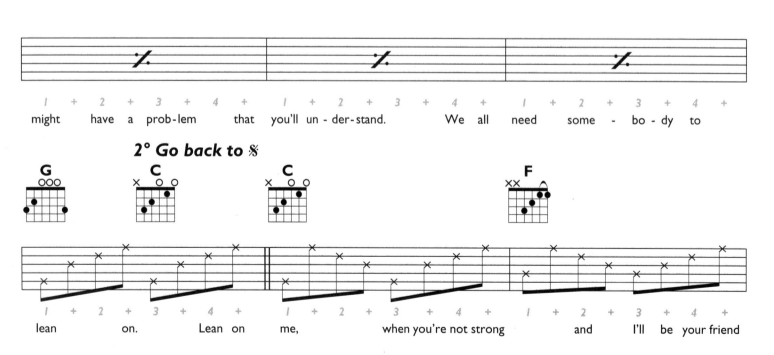

lean   on.   Lean on   me,   when you're not strong   and   I'll be your friend

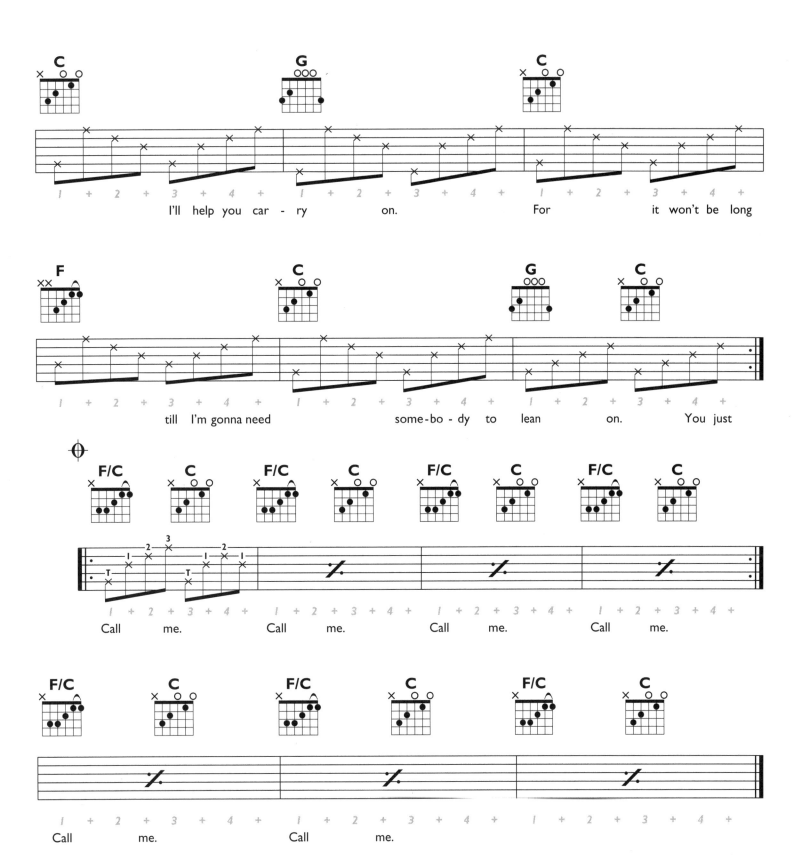

Verse 2:
If there is a load you have to bear
That you can't carry
I'm right up the road
I'll share your load
If you just call me.

VAN DIEMEN'S LAND

WORDS AND MUSIC BY DAVID EVANS, ADAM CLAYTON, PAUL HEWSON & LAURENCE MULLEN

The photo below shows how to play the **Bm** chord in this song. This is a barre chord shape, where you barre the second fret with your first finger.

There are quick chord changes in this song which only last for two notes – play these with your thumb and second finger as shown by the fingerings above the music.

To match the original recording, you will need to tune your guitar down a semitone.

This song features on U2's 1988 album Rattle And Hum, sung by guitarist The Edge (pictured above).

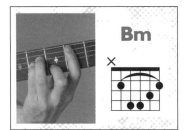

TUNE GUITAR DOWN A SEMITONE

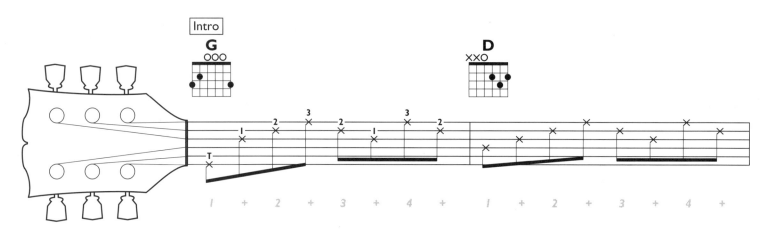

1. Hold   me   now

(Verses 2–4 see block lyrics)

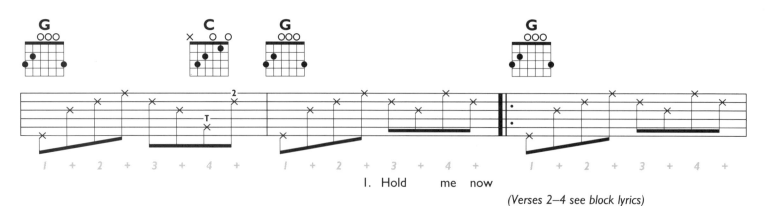

oh,   hold   me   now   till   this

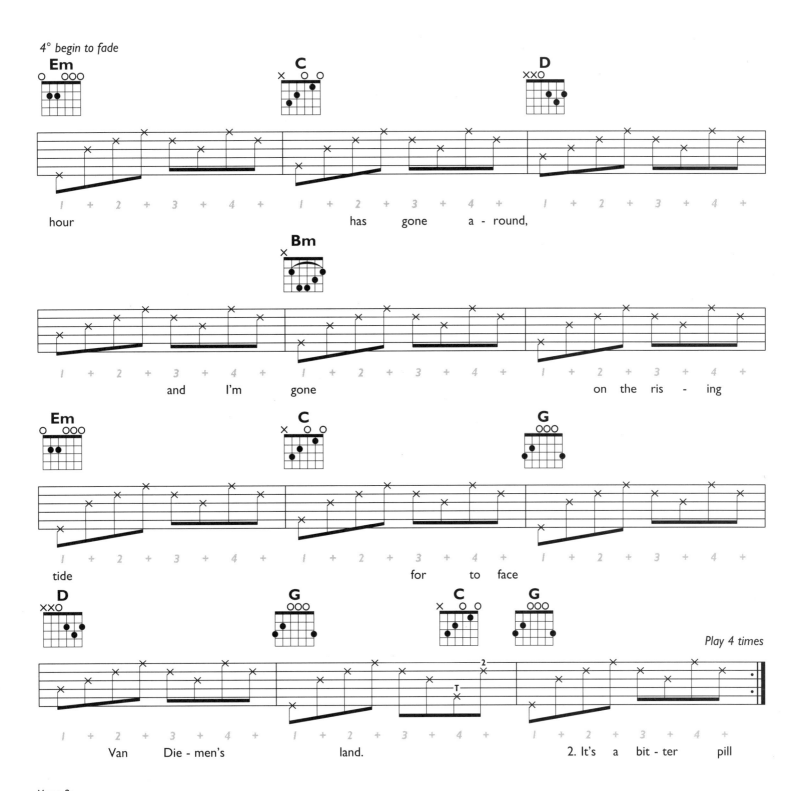

Verse 2:
It's a bitter pill I swallow here,
To be rent from one so dear.
We fought for justice and not for gain,
But the magistrate sent me away.

Verse 3:
Now kings will rule and the poor will toil,
And tear their hands as they tear the soil.
But a day will come in this dawning age,
When an honest man sees an honest wage.

Verse 4:
Hold me now, oh, hold me now.
Till this hour has gone around.
And I'm gone on the rising tide,
For to face Van Diemen's land.

YESTERDAY

WORDS AND MUSIC BY JOHN LENNON & PAUL McCARTNEY

This might seem like a simple song, but as you'll see, it is very sophisticated in terms of the many chords that it uses. Chords such as **Bm⁷**, **D⁷** and **G⁷** are very 'colourful' compared to the **Bm**, **D** and **G** shapes used in previous songs. As ever, start slowly, and practise shifting between each chord shape before working on the picking pattern.

Yesterday is one of the most covered songs of all time. The Beatles' original version was included on their Help! album in 1965.

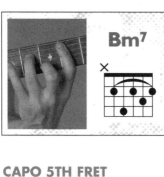 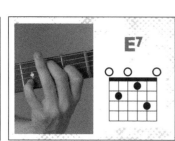 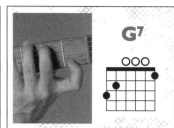 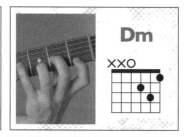

CAPO 5TH FRET

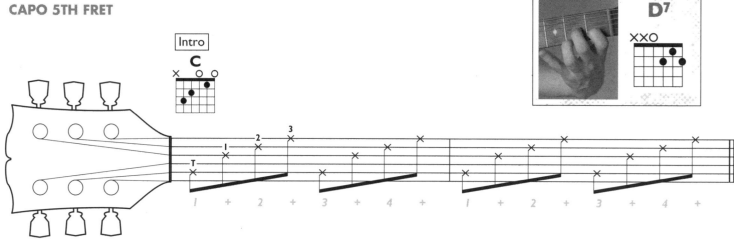

1. Yes - ter - day,   all   my   trou - bles   seemed   so
(Verse 4 see block lyrics)

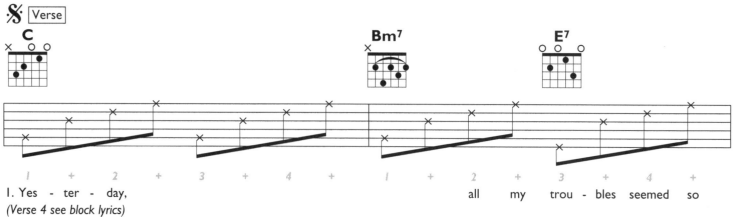

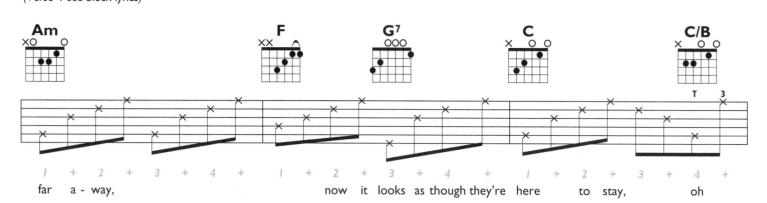

far   a - way,   now   it   looks   as   though   they're   here   to   stay,   oh

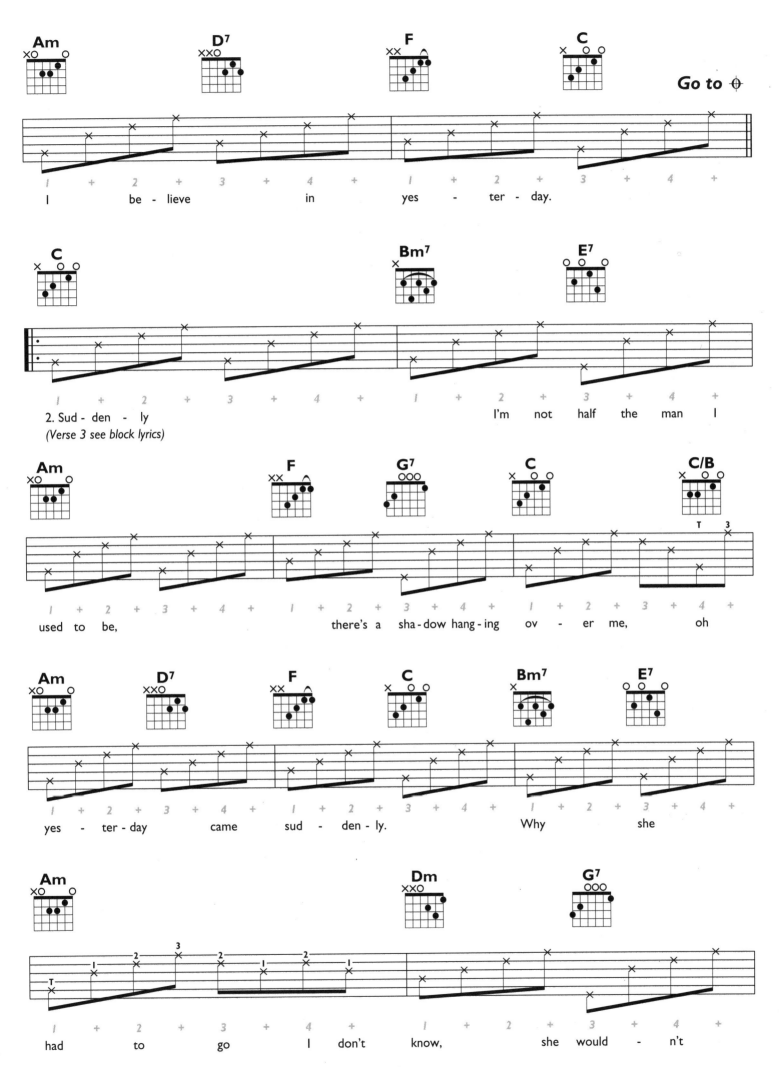

Go to ⊕

I be - lieve in yes - ter - day.

2. Sud - den - ly
(Verse 3 see block lyrics)

I'm not half the man I

used to be, there's a sha - dow hang - ing ov - er me, oh

yes - ter - day came sud - den - ly. Why she

had to go I don't know, she would - n't

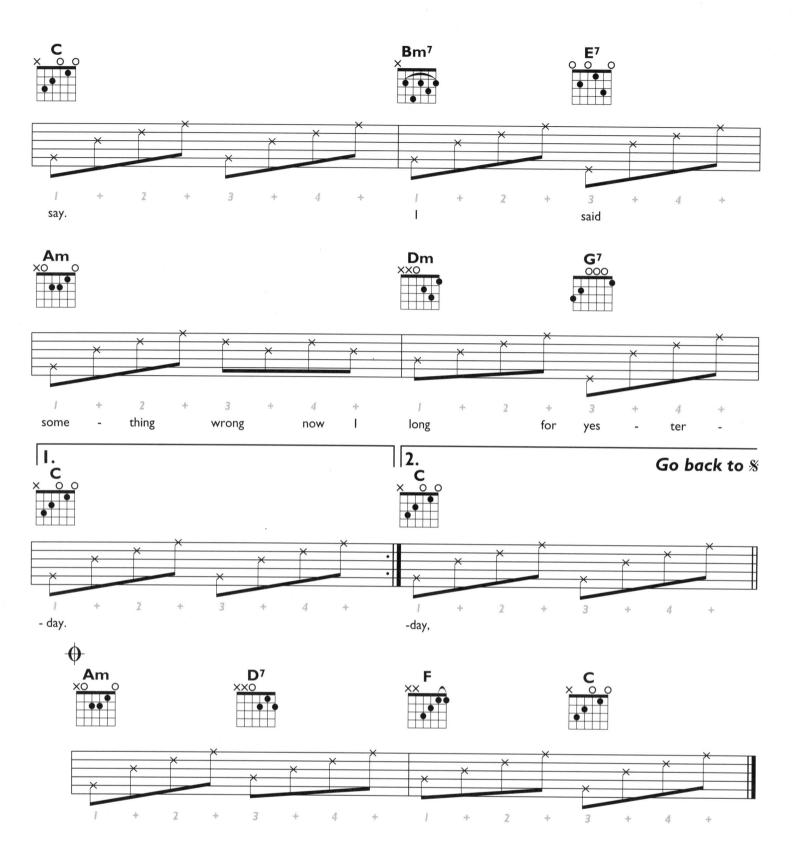

Verses 3 & 4:
Yesterday,
Love was such an easy game to play.
Now I need a place to hide away,
Oh, I believe
In yesterday.

GIRL OF THE NORTH COUNTRY

WORDS AND MUSIC BY BOB DYLAN

This Bob Dylan classic uses a pattern picking two strings at once, in different combinations (see photo, right). Practise switching between the **A** and **D/A** chords with your fretting hand, and then work on the picking pattern.

Look out for the bars with just two rhythm counts.

Hand position for the first picking pattern.

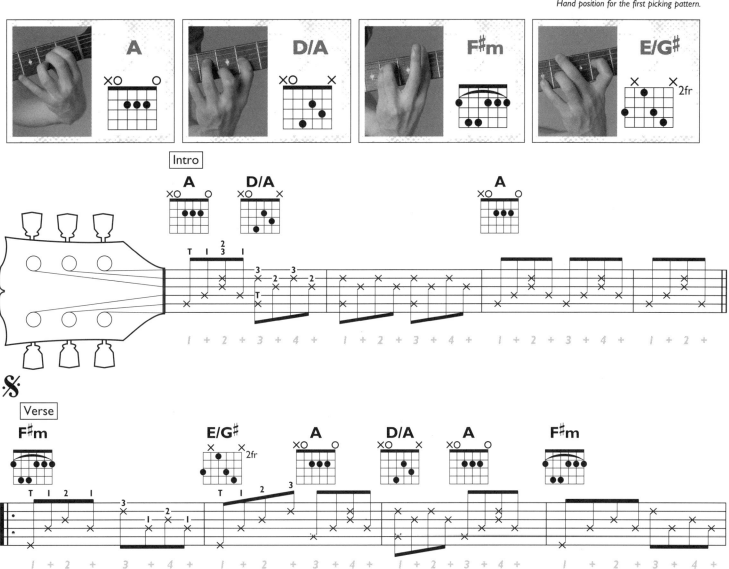

1. Well,   if you're trav-'lin in the north   coun-try fair,   where the wind hits hea-vy   on the
(Verses 2, 3, 4 & 5 see block lyrics)

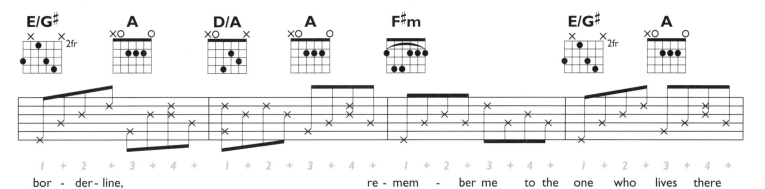

bor - der - line,   re - mem - ber me   to the   one   who   lives there

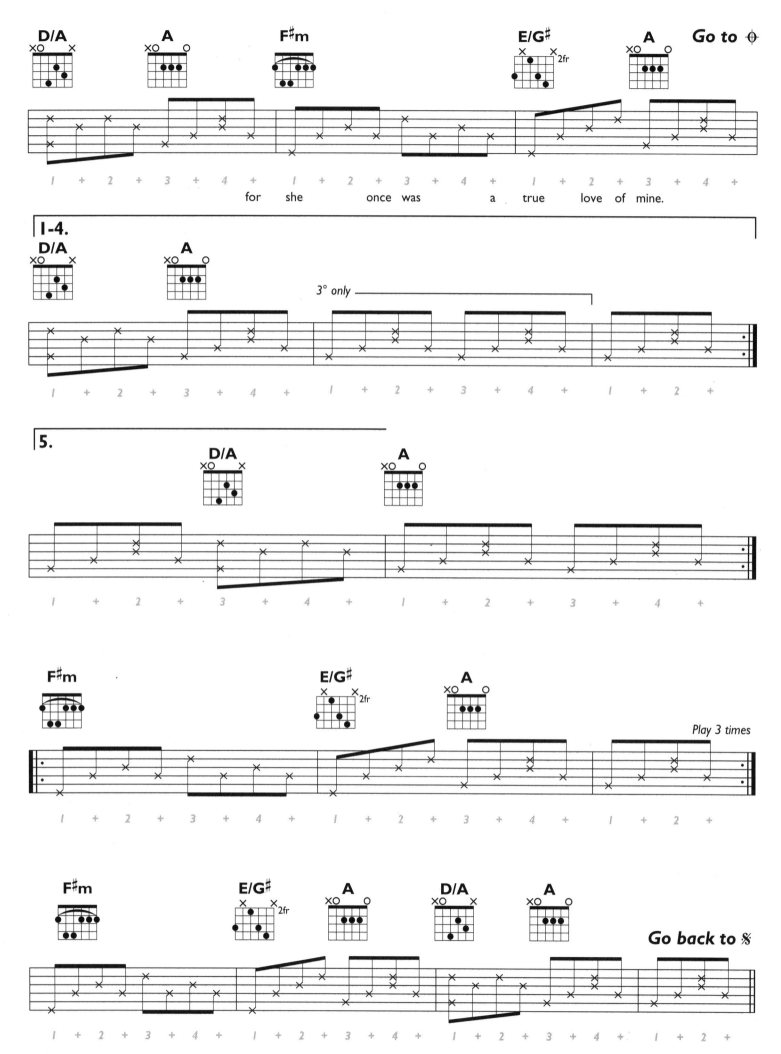

for she once was a true love of mine.

Go to ⊕

Go back to 𝄋

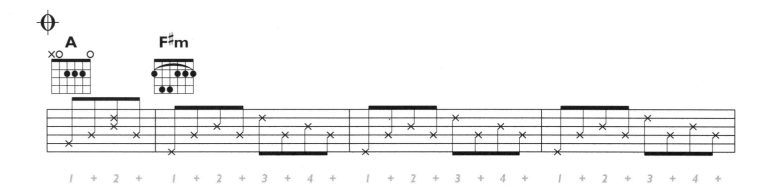

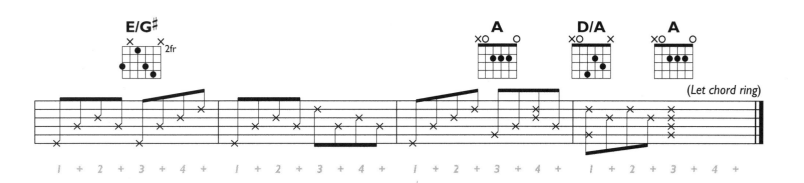

(Let chord ring)

Verse 2:
Well, if you go when the snowflakes storm,
When the rivers freeze and summer ends,
Please see if she's wearing a coat so warm,
To keep her from the howlin' winds.

Verse 3:
Please see for me if her hair hangs long,
If it rolls and flows all down her breast.
Please see for me if her hair hangs long,
That's the way I remember her best.

Verse 4:
I'm-a-wonderin' if she remembers me at all.
Many times I've often played
In the darkness of my night
In the brightness of my day.

Verse 5:
So if you're travelling in the north country fair,
Where the winds hit heavy on the borderline,
Remember me to the one who lives there
She once was a true love of mine.

IN MY ROOM

WORDS AND MUSIC BY BRIAN WILSON & GARY USHER

This song has six counts to each bar, with a rising and falling pattern for each chord. Watch for the quick changes in the bridge, where a new picking pattern is briefly used.

This song appeared on the Beach Boys' 1963 release Surfer Girl.

CAPO 2ND FRET

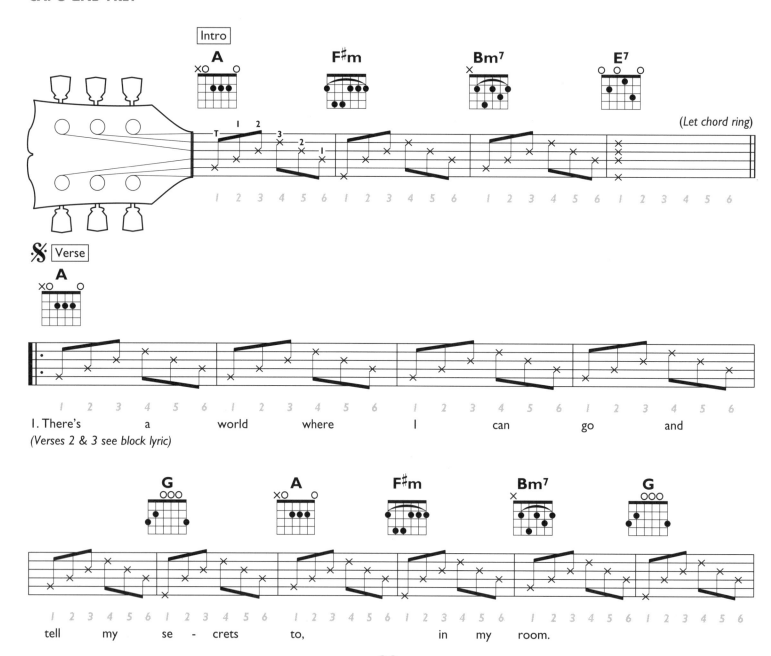

1. There's   a   world   where   I   can   go   and

(Verses 2 & 3 see block lyric)

tell   my   se - crets   to,   in   my   room.

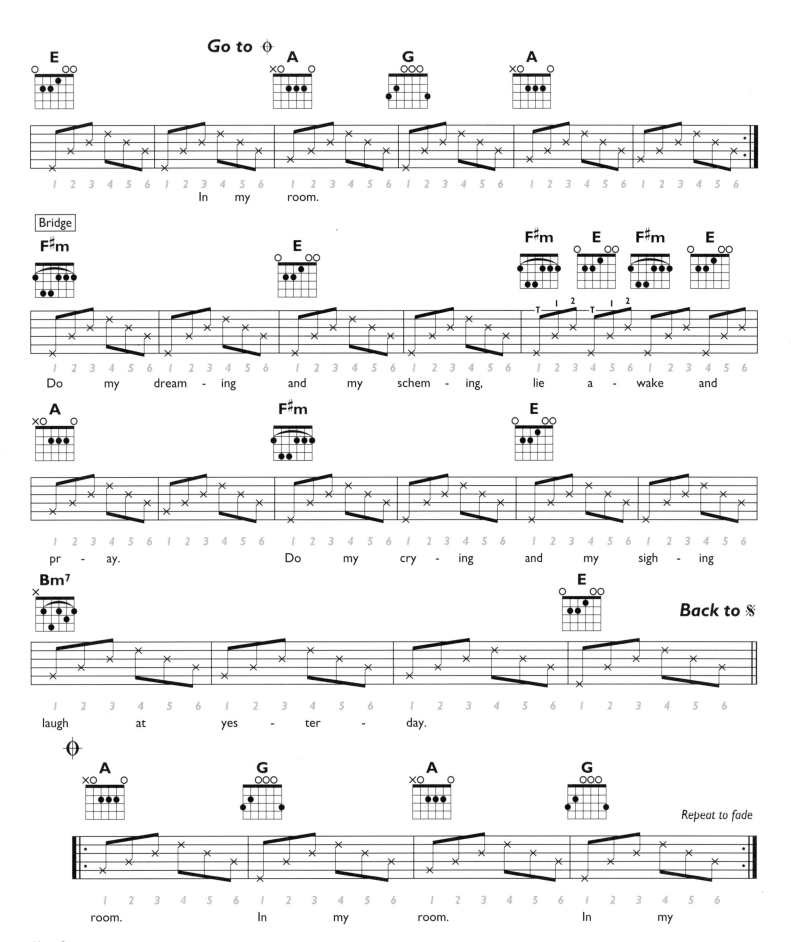

Verse 2:
In this world I lock out all my worries and my fears
In my room, in my room.

Verse 3:
Now it's dark and I'm alone but I won't be afraid
In my room, in my room.

FIELDS OF GOLD
WORDS AND MUSIC BY STING

The **Dsus⁴** (**D suspended 4th**) chord shown below alternates with **D** at the end of this song, creating tension before finally resolving.

This song was written by Sting for his Ten Summoners' Tales album in 1993. It has since been famously covered by Eva Cassidy.

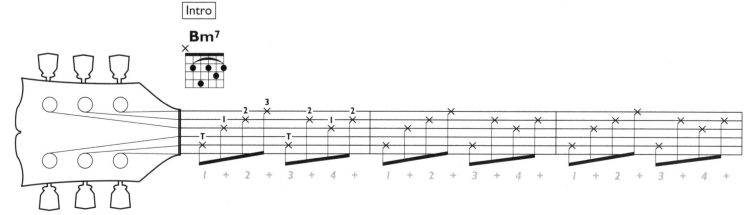

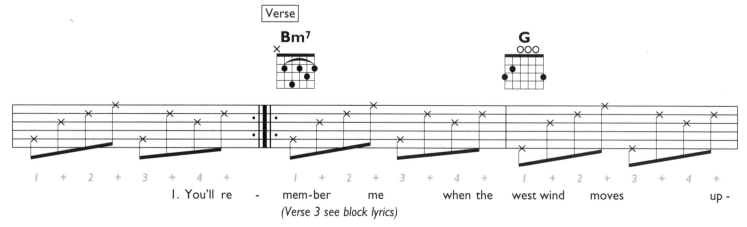

1. You'll re - mem-ber me   when the west wind moves   up-
(Verse 3 see block lyrics)

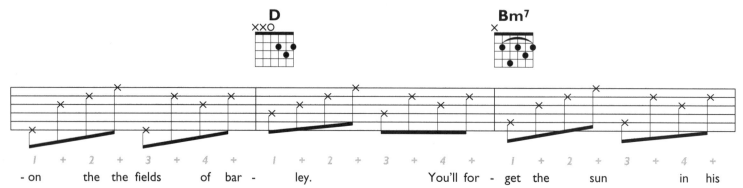

- on   the the fields of bar - ley.   You'll for - get the   sun   in his

30

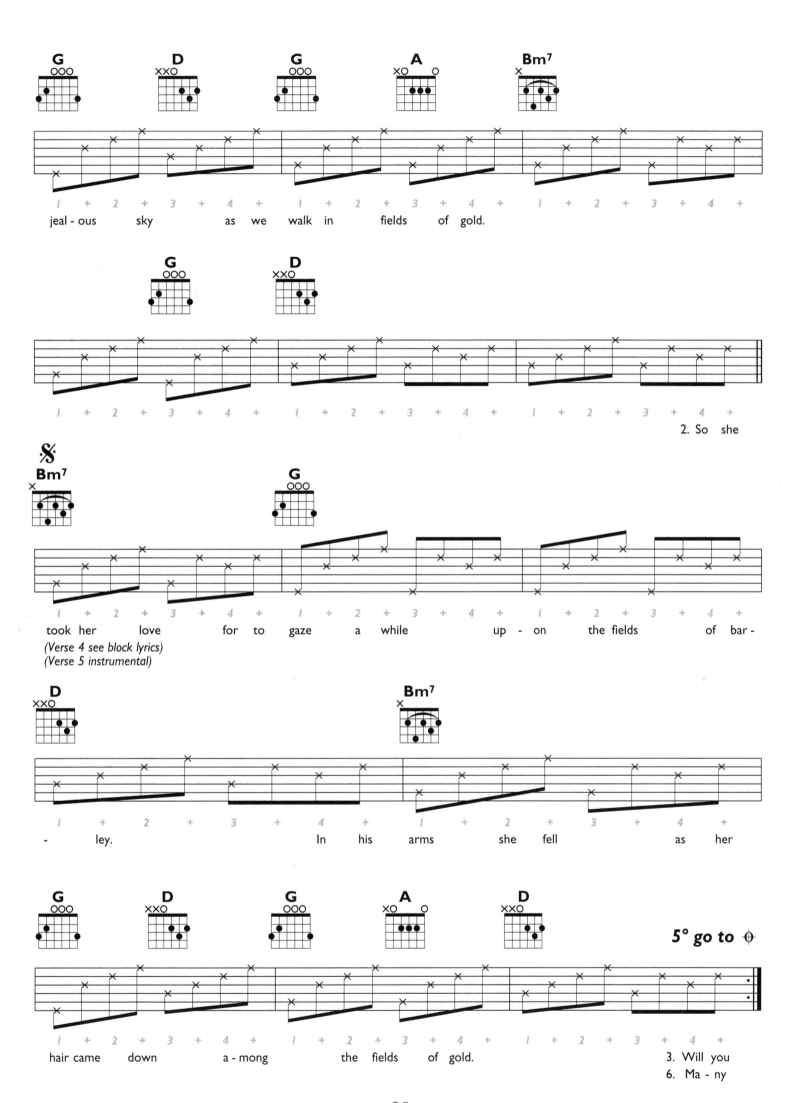

jeal - ous sky as we walk in fields of gold.

2. So she

took her love for to gaze a while up - on the fields of bar -

(Verse 4 see block lyrics)
(Verse 5 instrumental)

- ley. In his arms she fell as her

5° *go to* ⊕

hair came down a - mong the fields of gold.

3. Will you
6. Ma - ny

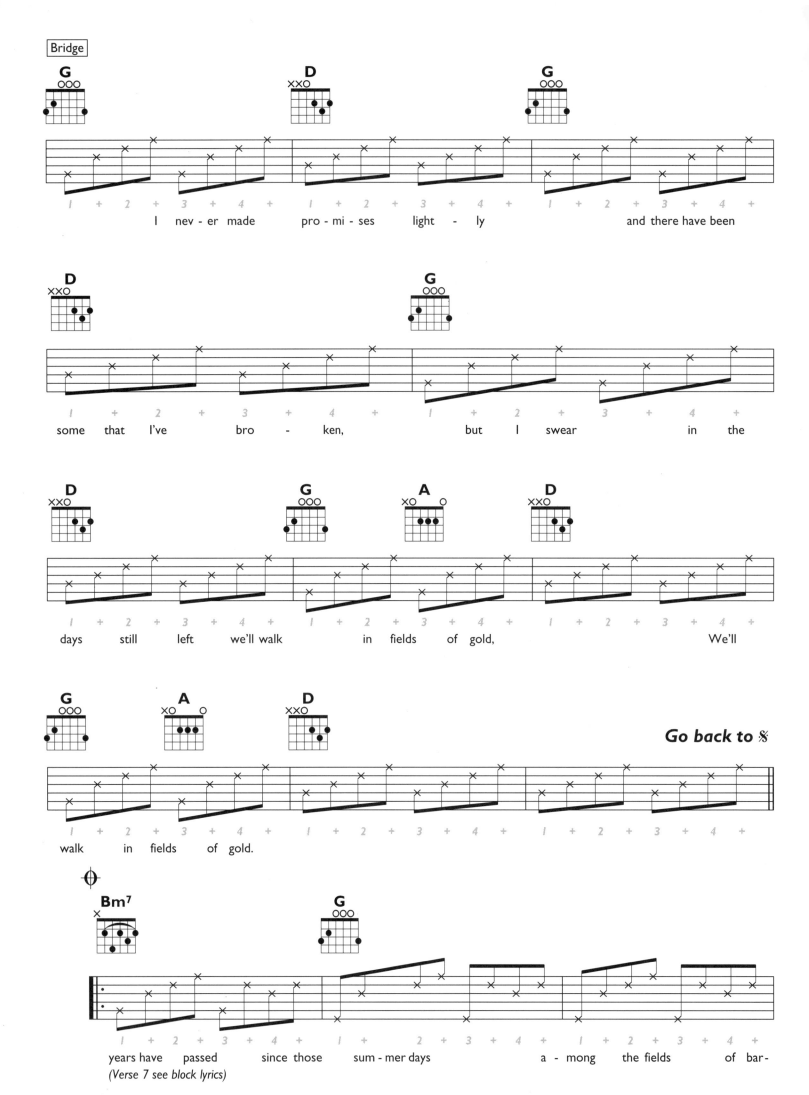

Go back to 𝄋

(Verse 7 see block lyrics)

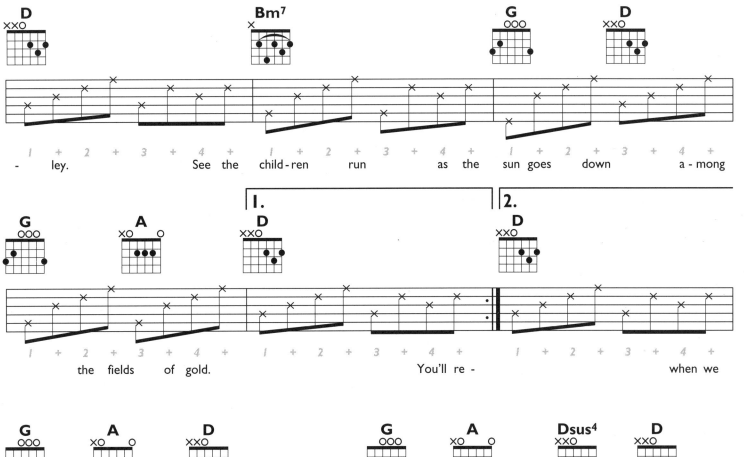

- ley.　See the child-ren run　as the sun goes down a - mong

the fields of gold.　You'll re -　when we

walked in fields of gold.　When we walked in fields of gold.

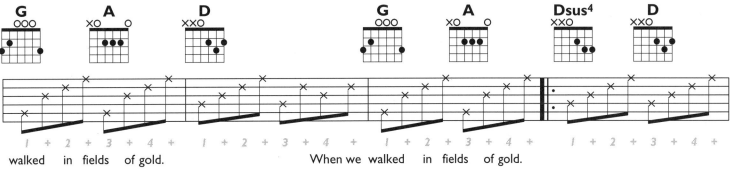

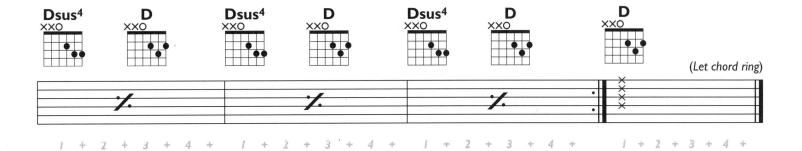

(Let chord ring)

Verse 3:
Will you stay with me, will you be my love,
Among the fields of barley?
We'll forget the sun in his jealous sky,
As we lie in fields of gold.

Verse 4:
See the west wind move like a lover so,
Upon the fields of barley.
Feel her body rise when you kiss her mouth,
Among the fields of gold.

Verse 7:
You'll remember me when the west wind moves,
Upon the fields of barley.
You can tell the sun in his jealous sky,
When we walked in fields of gold.

AMERICA

SONG BY JOHNNY BORRELL & ANDY BURROWS
MUSIC BY RAZORLIGHT

The **D(add⁴)** chord in this song is easier to play than it might sound; start with a **C** shape, and then slide that hand position up two frets.

Observe the crosses on the strings carefully for each chord shape. You won't always be picking the lowest note of the chord (for instance, for the **G** chord in the second bar).

Use a capo at the seventh fret to match the distinctive tone of the original recording.

Dadd⁴

CAPO 7TH FRET

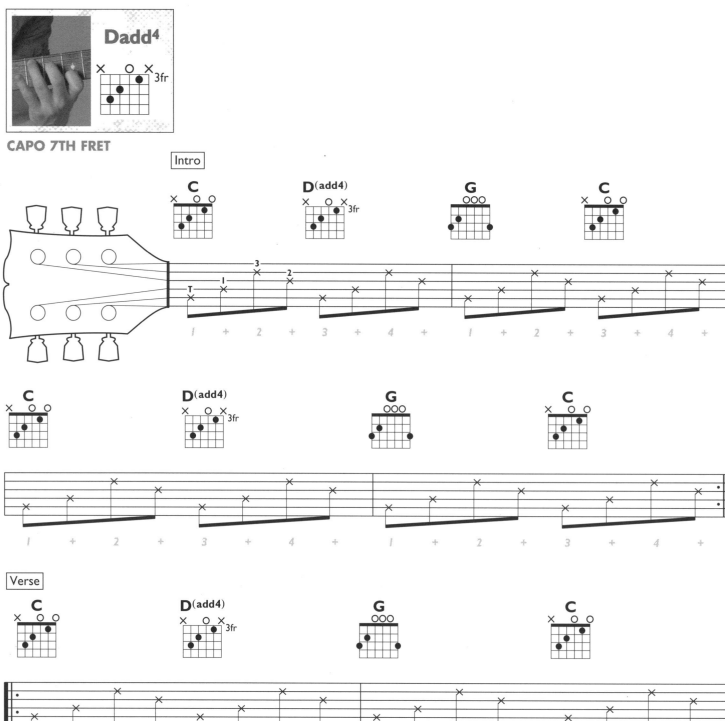

1. What a drag   it   is;   the shape I'm   in,
(Verse 2 see block lyrics)

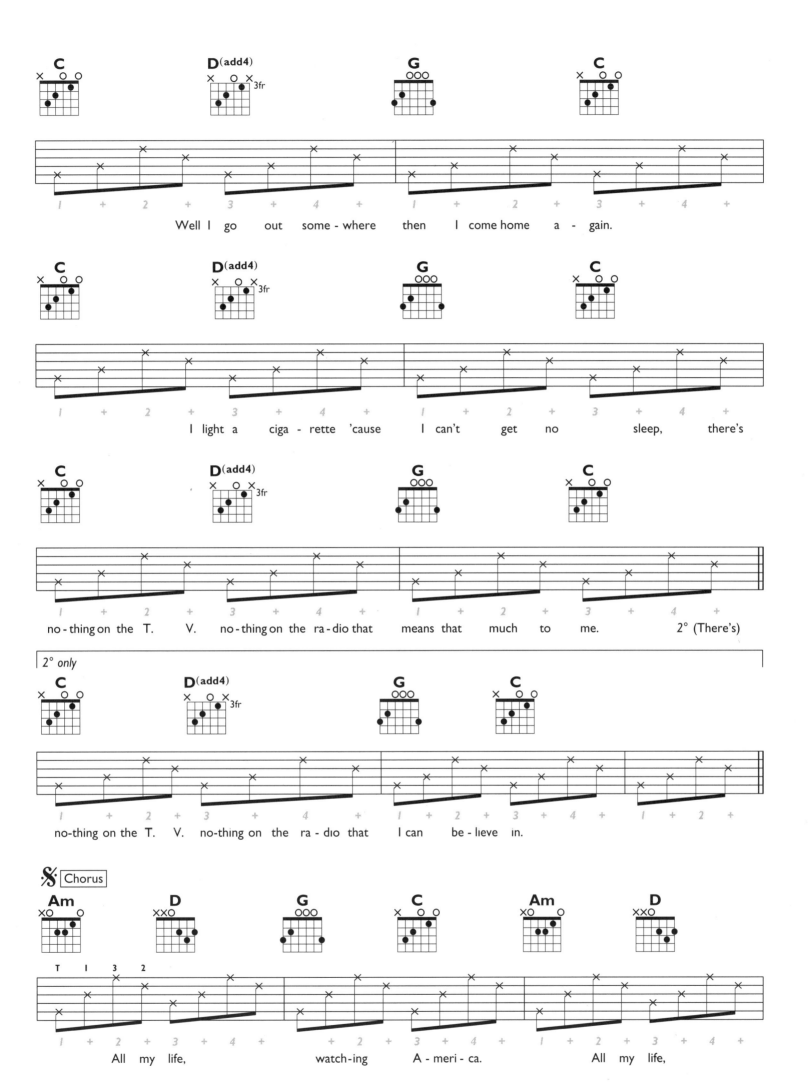

Well I go out some - where then I come home a - gain.

I light a ciga - rette 'cause I can't get no sleep, there's

no - thing on the T. V. no - thing on the ra - dio that means that much to me. 2° (There's)

2° only

no - thing on the T. V. no - thing on the ra - dio that I can be - lieve in.

Chorus

All my life, watch - ing A - meri - ca. All my life,

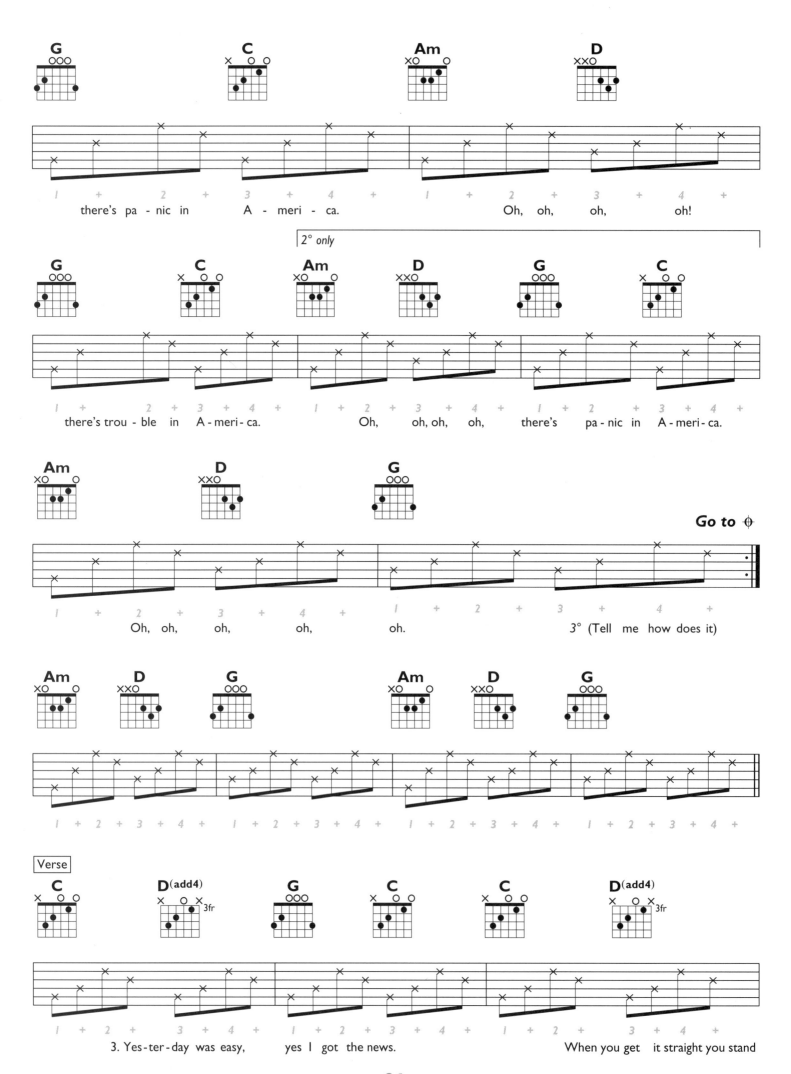

up you just can't lose.   Give you my confi-dence,   all my faith in   life.   Don't

stand   me up   don't let   me down, no, I   need you to - night.   To

hold   me,   say you'll be here.   To

hold   me,   say you'll be here.   To hold   me,

Go back to %

say you'll be here,   to   hold.

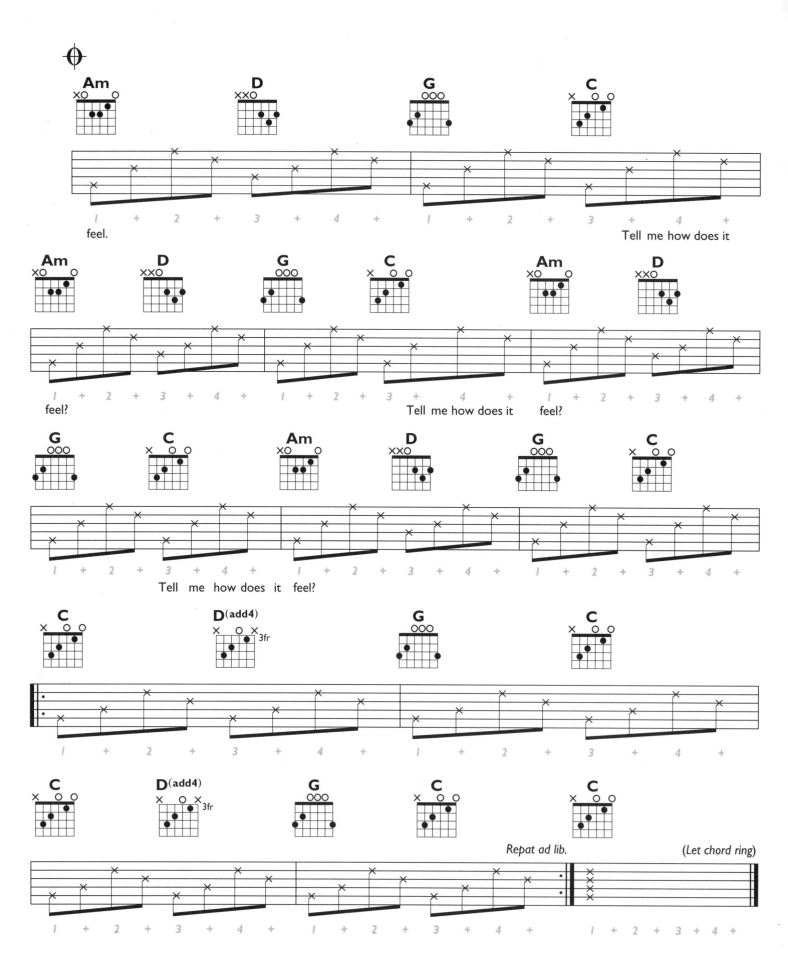

Verse 2:
Yesterday was easy, happiness came and went.
I got the movie script, but I don't know what it meant.
I light a cigarette 'cause I can't get no sleep
There's nothing on the T.V. nothing on the radio
That means that much to me
There's nothing on the T.V. nothing on the radio
That I can believe in.

HALLELUJAH
WORDS AND MUSIC BY LEONARD COHEN

Watch out for the variations on the picking patterns in this song. The **G** chord shape for this song is a little different from the shape used previously.

At the end of the song, the **N.C.** (No chord) symbol means that there is a pause before strumming the very last chord.

This song was written and recorded by Leonard Cohen in 1984, but has become famous through its performance by a wide selection of artists, including Rufus Wainwright, Bob Dylan, and most notably Jeff Buckley (above), whose version is the basis for this arrangement.

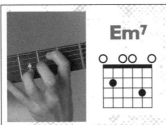

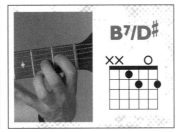

CAPO 5TH FRET

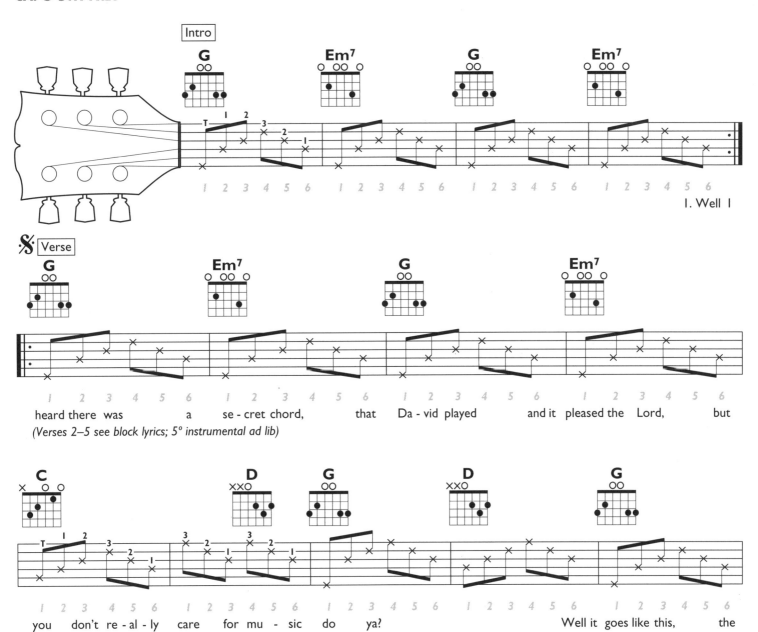

1. Well I

heard there was   a se-cret chord,   that Da-vid played   and it pleased the Lord,   but
(Verses 2–5 see block lyrics; 5° instrumental ad lib)

you don't re-al-ly care for mu-sic do ya?   Well it goes like this,   the

39

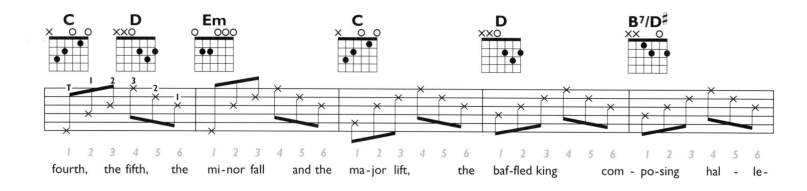

fourth, the fifth, the mi-nor fall and the ma-jor lift, the baf-fled king com-po-sing hal - le-

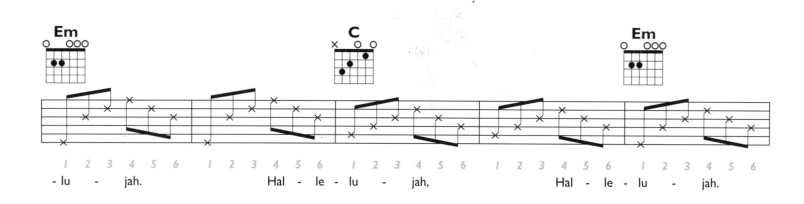

- lu - jah. Hal - le - lu - jah, Hal - le - lu - jah.

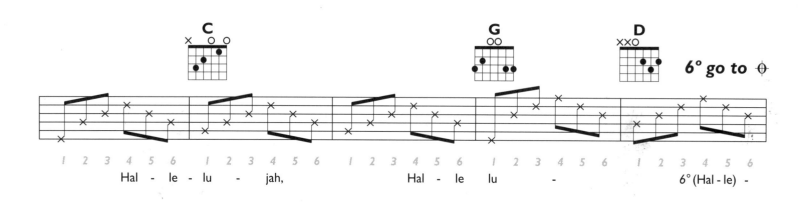

6° go to ⊕

Hal - le - lu - jah, Hal - le - lu - 6° (Hal - le) -

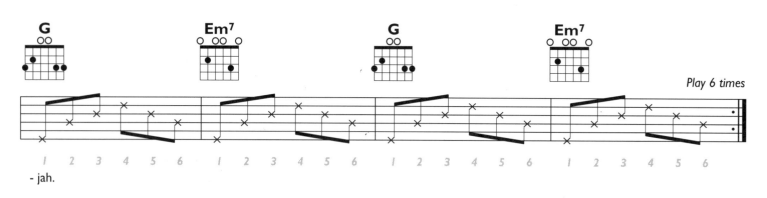

Play 6 times

- jah.

40

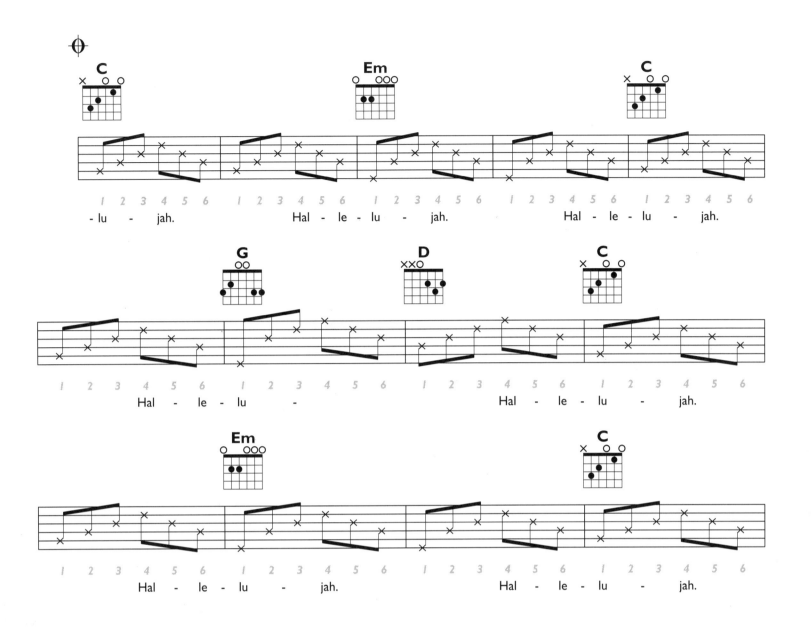

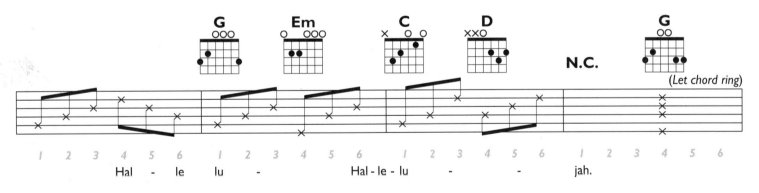

Verse 2:
Well, your faith was strong but you needed proof,
You saw her bathing on the roof,
Her beauty and the moonlight overthrew ya.
She tied you to her kitchen chair,
And she broke your throne and she cut your hair,
And from your lips you drew the hallelujah.

Verse 3:
Well, baby I've been here before,
I've seen this room and I've walked this floor,
You know I used to live alone before I knew ya.
And I've seen your flag on the marble arch,
And love is not a victory march,
It's a cold and it's a broken hallelujah.

Verse 4:
Well, there was a time when you let me know,
What's really going on below,
But now you never show that to me do ya?
But remember when I moved in you,
And the holy dove was moving too,
And every breath we drew was hallelujah.

Verse 5:
Well, maybe there's a God above,
But all I've ever learned from love,
Was how to shoot somebody who outdrew ya.
And it's not a cry that you hear at night,
It's not somebody who's seen the light,
It's a cold and it's a broken hallelujah.

HAVE I TOLD YOU LATELY

WORDS AND MUSIC BY VAN MORRISON

Major seventh (**maj⁷**) chords have a distinctive sound – compare the **Fmaj⁷** shape below with the **F** chords used previously (e.g. on page 4). The **G¹¹** shape might be a little tricky at first; check the fingering shown in the photos below to see how to switch to this chord from the preceeding **F** shape.

This Van Morrison song has become a popular 'first dance' for couples at weddings, belying its original spiritual meaning.

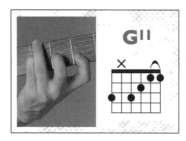

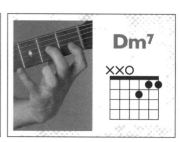
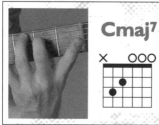

CAPO 4TH FRET

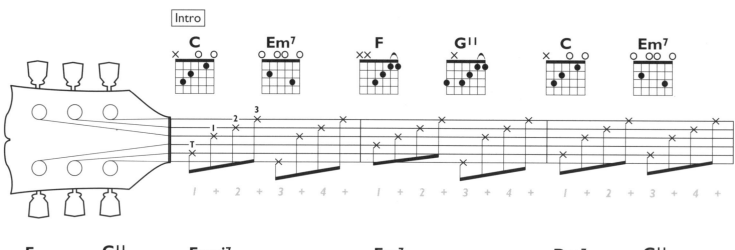

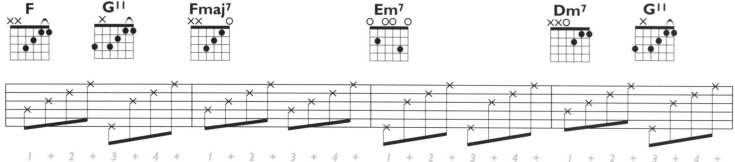

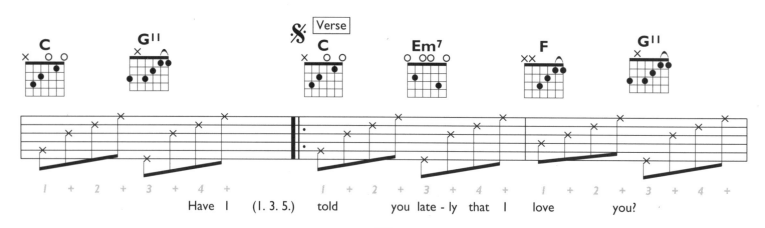

Have I (1. 3. 5.) told   you late - ly   that I   love   you?

42

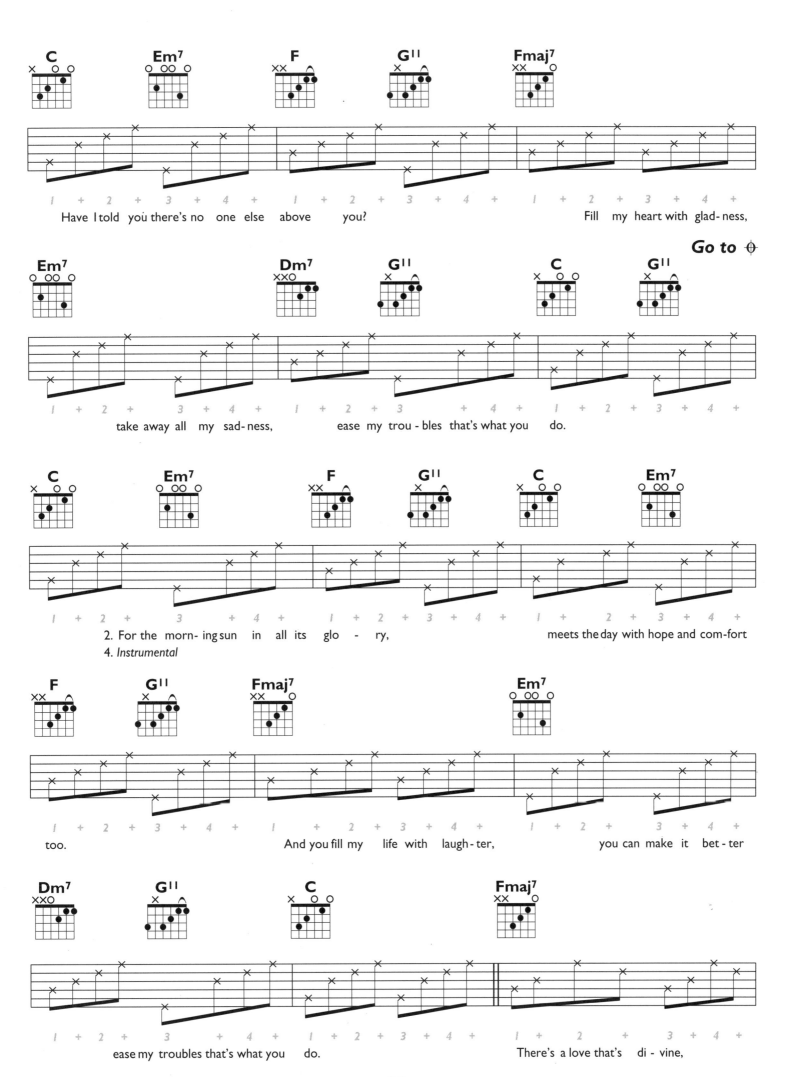

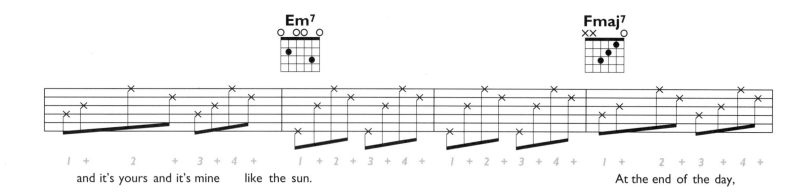

and it's yours and it's mine   like the sun.   At the end of the day,

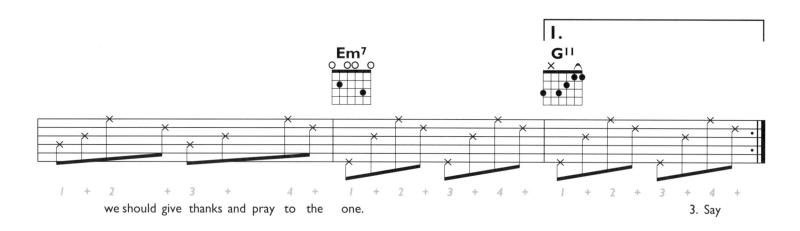

we should give thanks and pray to the   one.   3. Say

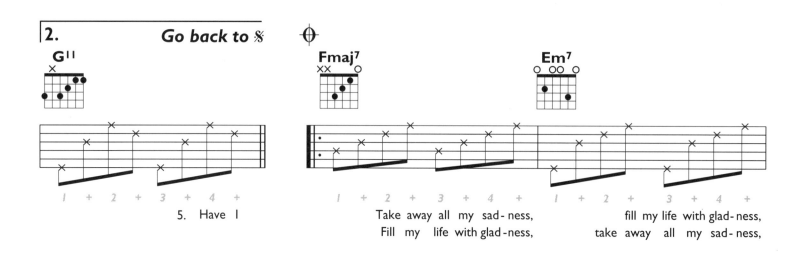

5. Have I

Take away all my sad - ness,   fill my life with glad - ness,
Fill my life with glad - ness,   take away all my sad - ness,

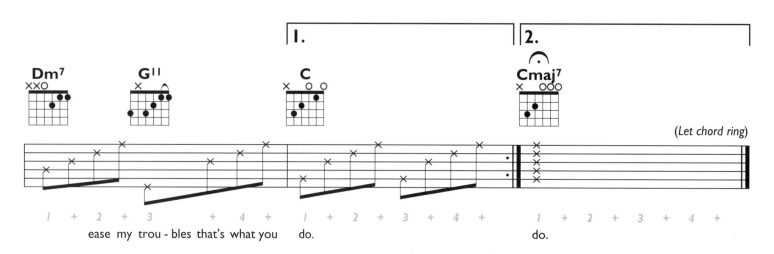

ease my trou - bles that's what you   do.   do.

IF YOU COULD READ MY MIND

WORDS AND MUSIC BY GORDON LIGHTFOOT

Practise changing smoothly between the chords of **G** and **Dm/F** before working on the picking pattern for this song.

Artists as diverse as Tori Amos and Olivia Newton-John have covered this 1970 hit by Gordon Lightfoot (above).

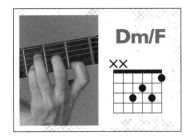

CAPO 2ND FRET

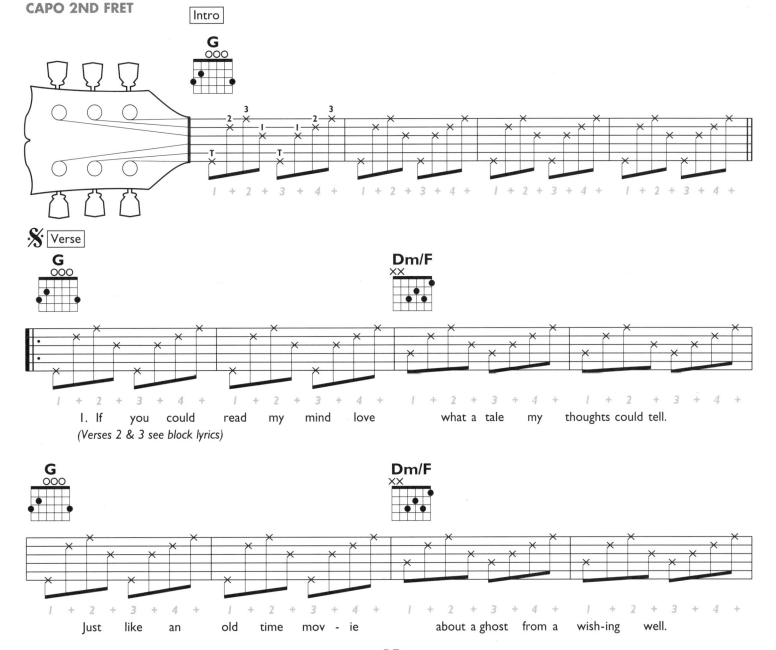

1. If you could read my mind love   what a tale my thoughts could tell.

(Verses 2 & 3 see block lyrics)

Just like an old time mov - ie   about a ghost from a wish-ing well.

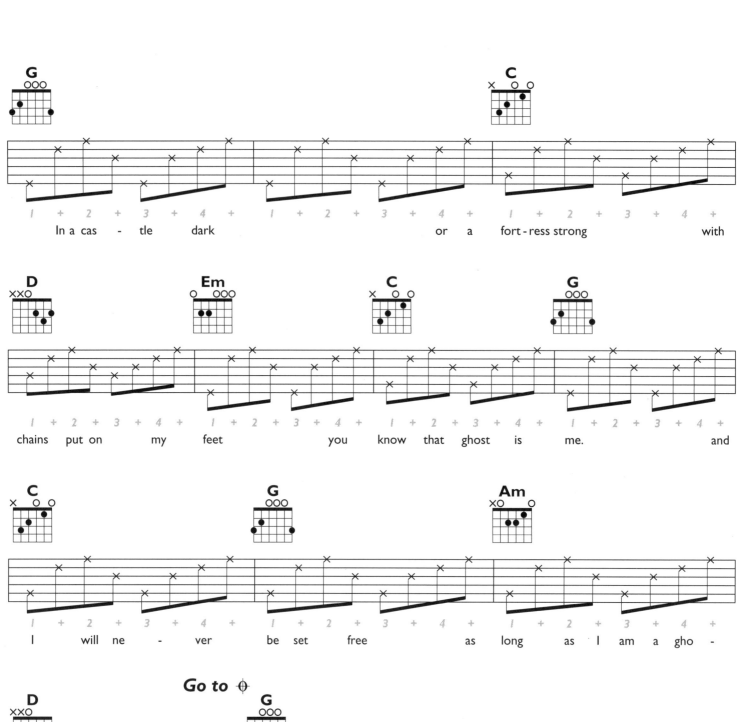

In a cas - tle dark or a fort - ress strong with chains put on my feet you know that ghost is me. and I will ne - ver be set free as long as I am a gho -

Go to

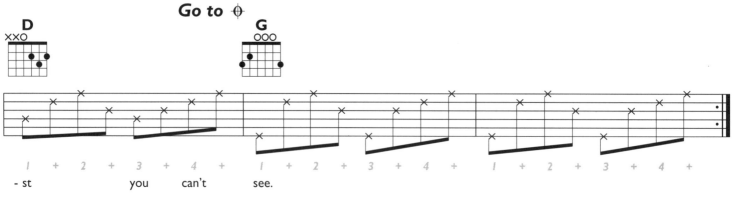

- st you can't see.

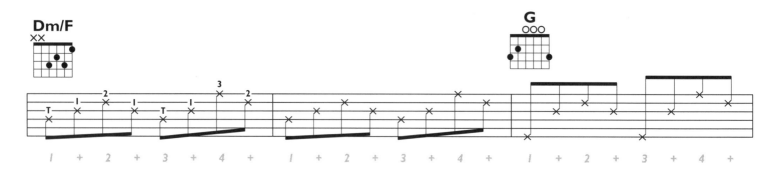

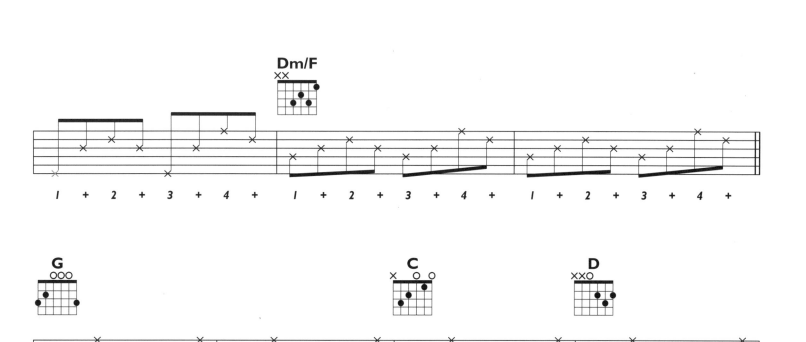

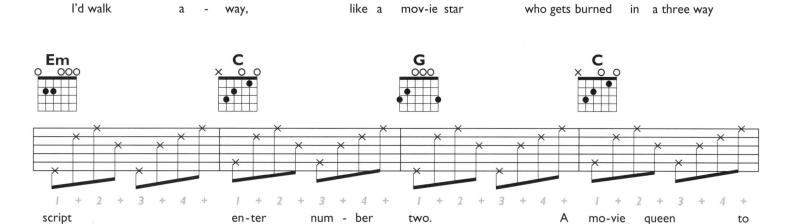

I'd walk a - way, like a mov-ie star who gets burned in a three way

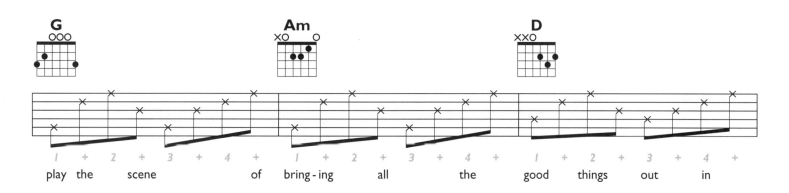

script en-ter num - ber two. A mo-vie queen to

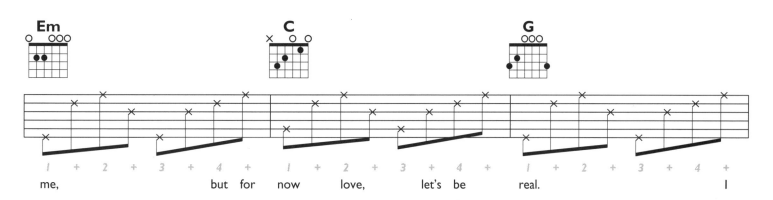

play the scene of bring-ing all the good things out in

me, but for now love, let's be real. I

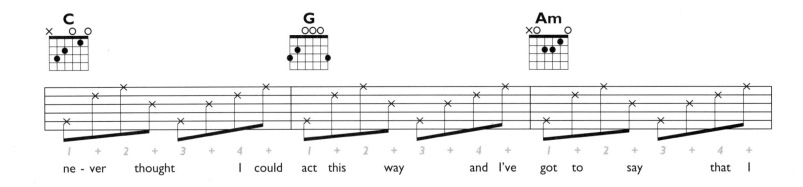

ne - ver   thought   I   could   act   this   way   and   I've   got   to   say   that   I

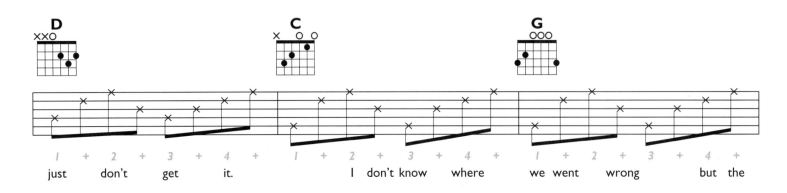

just   don't   get   it.   I   don't   know   where   we   went   wrong   but   the

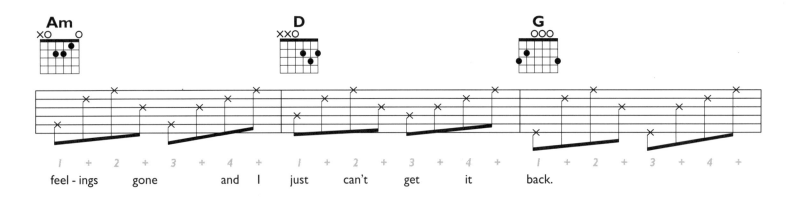

feel - ings   gone   and   I   just   can't   get   it   back.

Go back to 𝄋

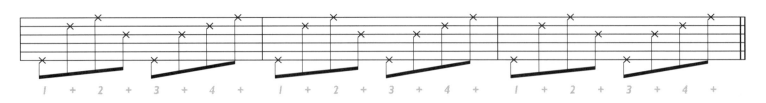

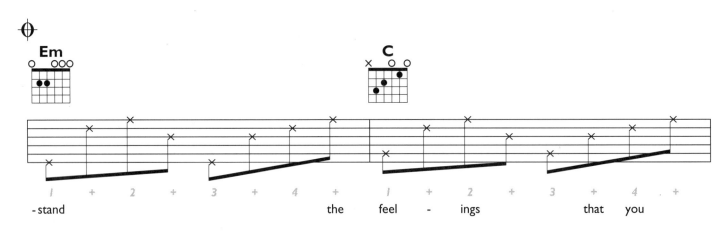

- stand   the   feel - ings   that   you

48

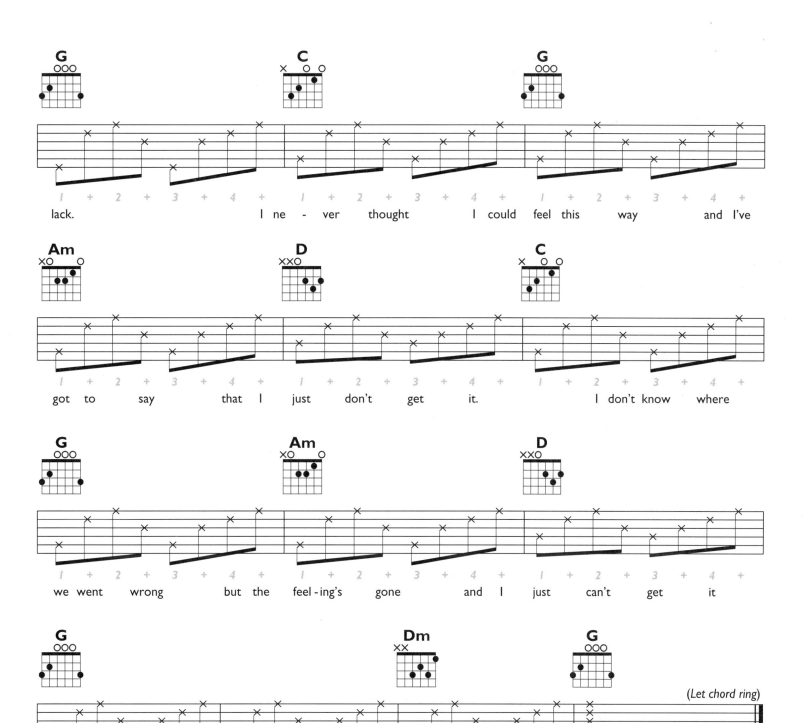

lack.   I ne - ver thought   I could feel this   way   and I've

got to say   that I just don't get   it.   I don't know where

we went wrong   but the feel-ing's gone   and I just can't get   it

(Let chord ring)

back.

Verse 2:
If I could read your mind love
What a tale your thoughts could tell
Just like a paperback novel
The kind that drugstores sell
When you reach the part where the heartaches come
The hero would be me
But heroes often fail
And you won't read that book again
Because the ending's just too hard to take.

Verse 3:
If you could read my mind love
What a tale my thoughts could tell
Just like an old time movie
'Bout a ghost from a wishin' well
In a castle dark or a fortress strong
With chains upon my feet
But stories always end
And if you read between the lines
Youll know that I'm just tryin' to understand
The feelin's that you lack
I never thought I could feel this way
And I've got to say that I just to get it
I don't know where we went wrong
But the feelin's gone
And I just can't get it back.

BABYLON
WORDS AND MUSIC BY DAVID GRAY

This song was first released on David Gray's White Ladder album in 1999.

The new chords for this song are **Dmaj⁷** and **Esus⁴**. Play **Dmaj⁷** by barring with your 1st finger. The **Esus⁴** chord is used for a short interlude before the second verse.

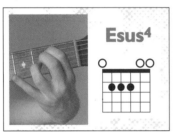

CAPO 2ND FRET

Intro

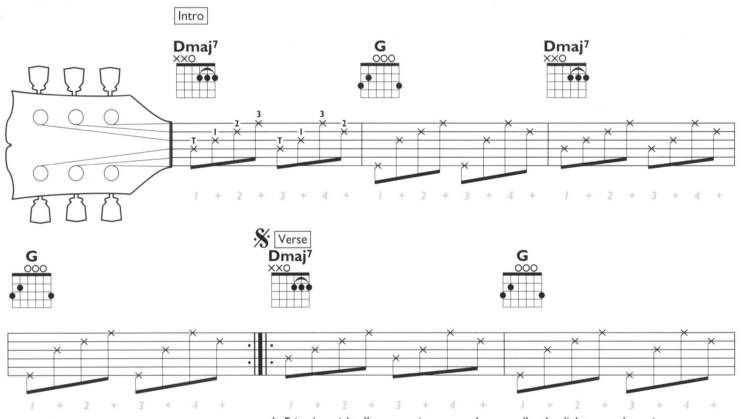

Verse

1. Fri - day night I'm go - ing no - where, all the lights are chang-ing
(Verses 2 & 3 see block lyrics)

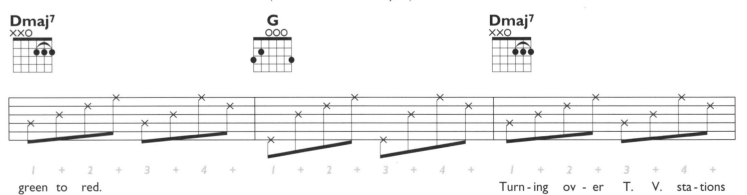

green to red.   Turn - ing ov - er T. V. sta - tions

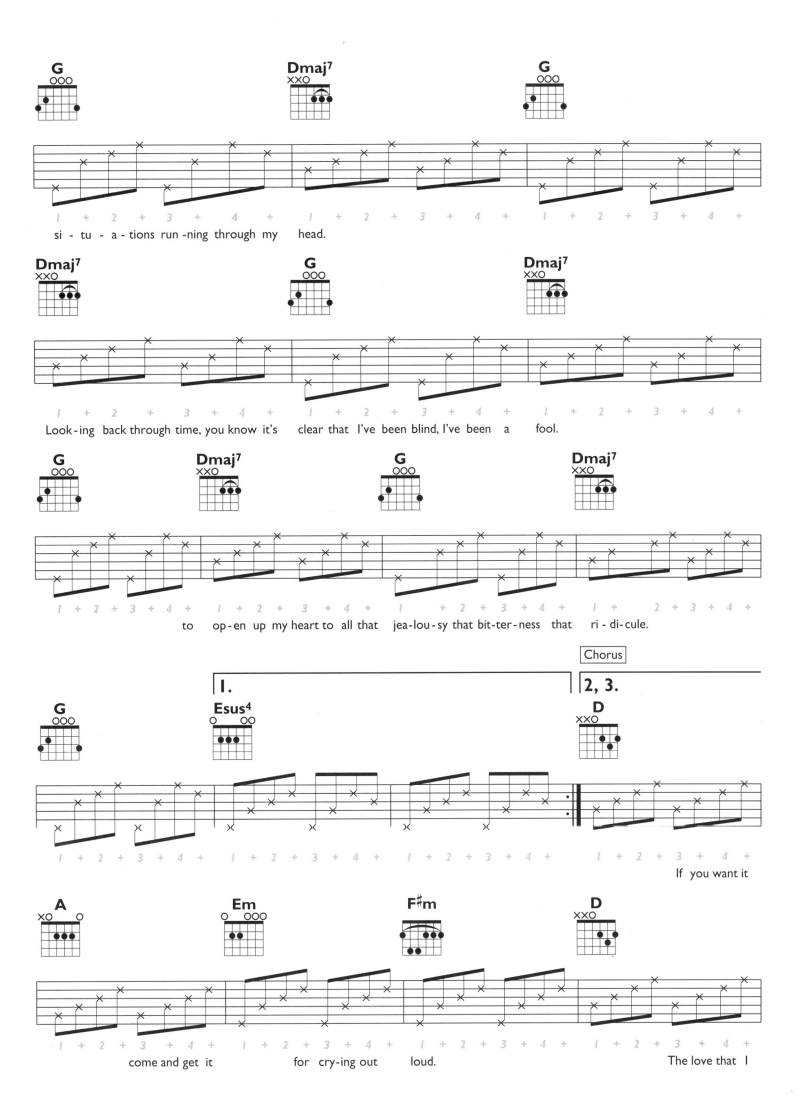

si - tu - a - tions run - ning through my head.

Look - ing back through time, you know it's clear that I've been blind, I've been a fool.

to op - en up my heart to all that jea - lou - sy that bit - ter - ness that ri - di - cule.

Chorus

1.

2, 3.

If you want it

come and get it   for cry - ing out   loud.   The love that I

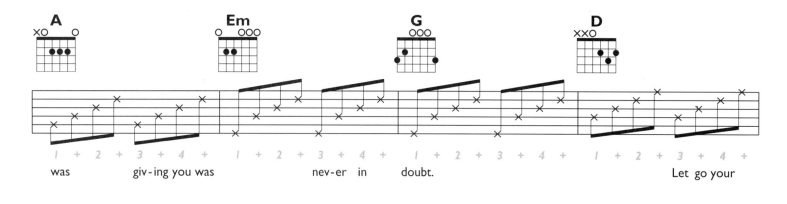

was   giv-ing you was   nev-er in   doubt.   Let go your

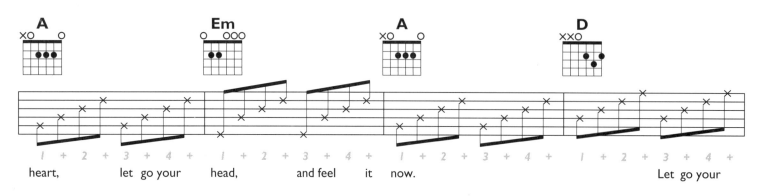

heart,   let go your   head,   and feel   it   now.   Let go your

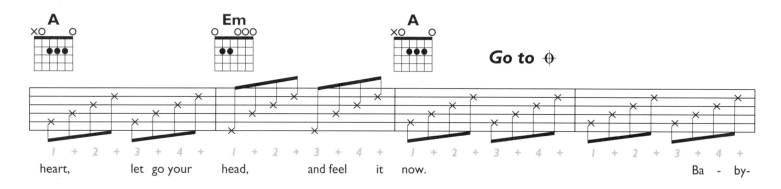

heart,   let go your   head,   and feel   it   now.   Ba - by-

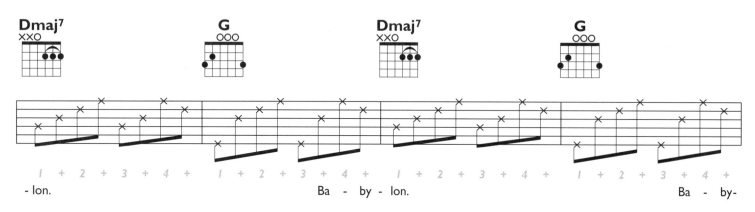

- lon.   Ba - by - lon.   Ba - by-

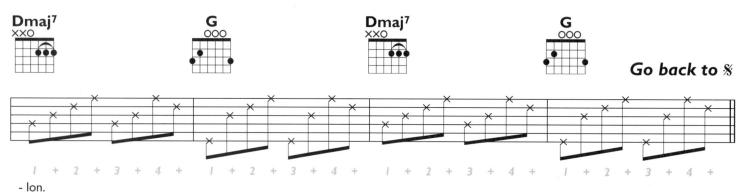

- lon.

52

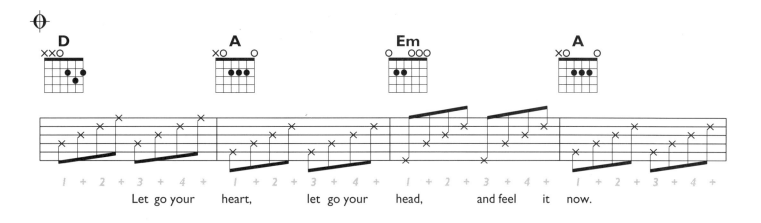

Let go your heart, let go your head, and feel it now.

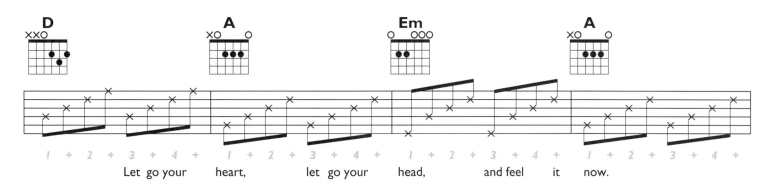

Let go your heart, let go your head, and feel it now.

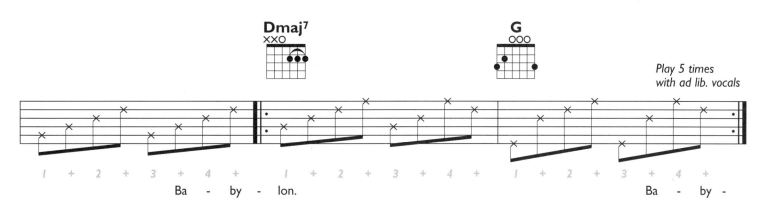

*Play 5 times
with ad lib. vocals*

Ba - by - lon. Ba - by -

(Let chord ring)

Verse 2:
Saturday I'm running wild,
And all the lights are changing red to green.
Moving through the crowd I'm pushing,
Chemicals all rushing through my bloodstream.
Only wish that you were here,
You know I'm seeing it so clear,
I've been afraid.
To tell you how I really feel,
Admit to some of those bad mistakes I've made.

Verse 3:
Sunday all the lights of London,
Shining, sky is fading red to blue.
I'm kicking through the autumn leaves,
And wondering where it is you might be going to.
Turning back for home,
You know I'm feeling so alone,
I can't believe.
Climbing on the stair,
I turn around to see you smiling there,
In front of me.

CRAZY

WORDS AND MUSIC BY WILLIE NELSON

This song has a lot of chords: **G**, **C**, **Bm**, **Am**, **D^7**, **E^7**, **G$\sharp$dim^7**, **C$\sharp$dim^7**, **E$\flat$^{7}**, **A$\flat$**, **F^7**, **B$\flat$m**, **D$\flat$**, **Cm** and **Adim^7**. It might seem that it would take a long time to learn all of these; however, many of them use the same chord shape, played in different positions. For instance, once you can play **Bm,** you can slide that chord down a fret to easily play **B$\flat$m,** or up a fret to play **Cm.** Follow the chord boxes above the music.

Diminished (**dim**) chords have a particular sound full of tension, and they are used in this song to create dramatic links between the other chords. The shape to play for **Adim^7** is the same as **G$\sharp$dim^7**, moved up a fret.

Note that the **Am** and **D^7** chords have a particular picking pattern, where the thumbed note alternates between open strings to produce a country-style bass line.

Willie Nelson wrote this country classic in 1961, and it was first recorded by Patsy Cline (pictured).

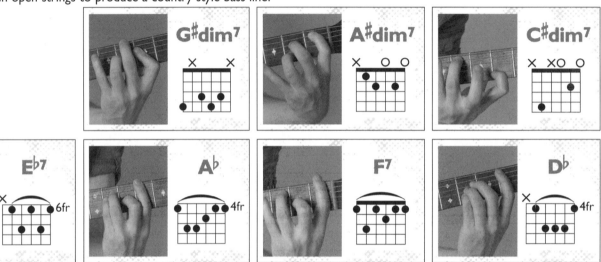

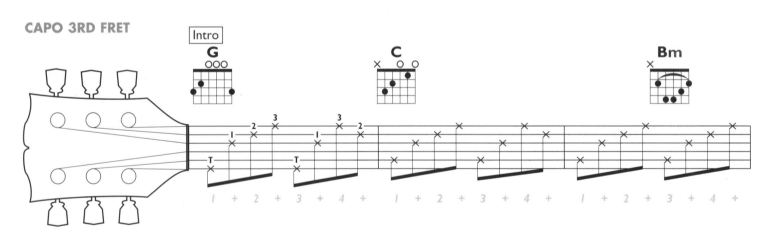

CAPO 3RD FRET

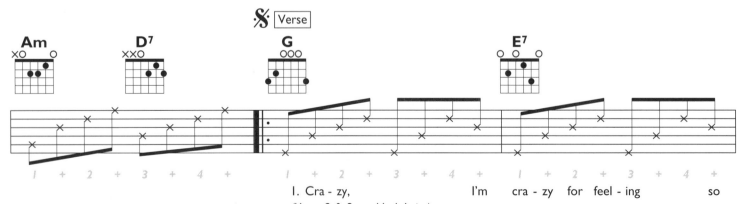

1. Cra - zy,   I'm cra - zy for feel - ing   so

(Verse 2 & 3 see block lyrics)

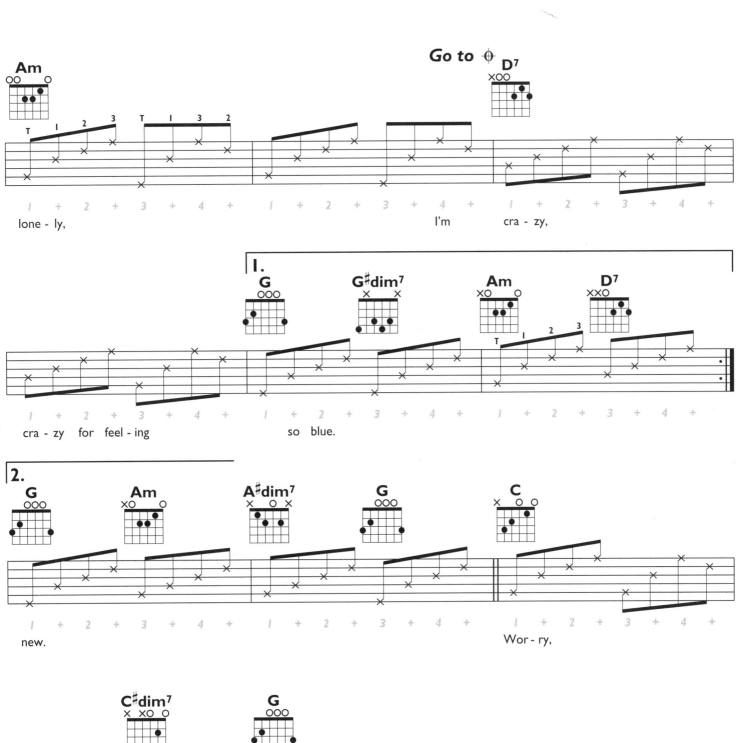

lone - ly,   I'm cra - zy,

cra - zy for feel - ing   so blue.

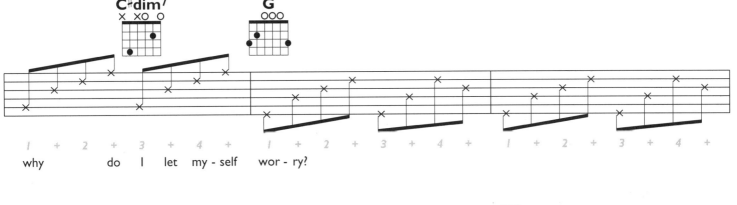

new.   Wor - ry,

why   do I   let my - self wor - ry?

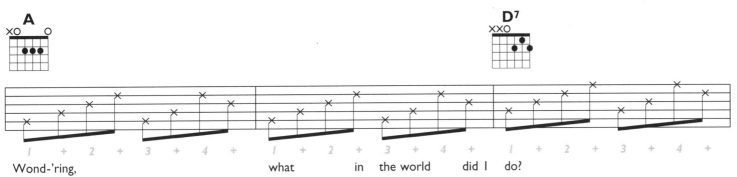

Wond-'ring,   what   in the world did I do?

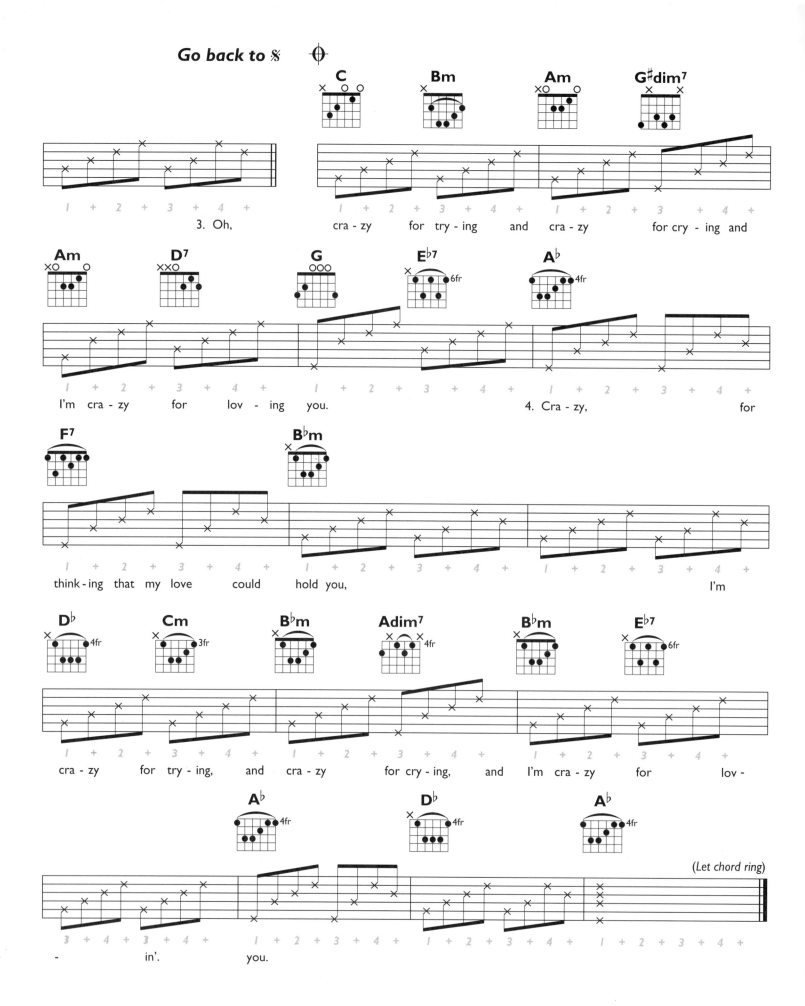

Verse 2:
I knew you'd love me as long as you wanted
And then someday you'd leave me for somebody new.

Verse 3:
Crazy, for thinkin' that my love could hold you.
I'm crazy for tryin', and crazy for cryin',
And I'm crazy for loving you!

THE BOXER
WORDS AND MUSIC BY PAUL SIMON

This song has a bass line played with the thumb on alternating strings, and uses a special shape for **C**. Listen for the progression from **G** to **G⁷** to **G⁶** (this chord is shown below).

Look out for the quick changes from **C** to **G** to **Am** later in the song.

This song was released on this classic 1970 Simon and Garfunkel album.

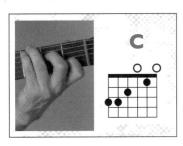

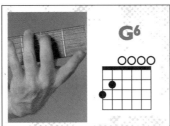

TUNE GUITAR DOWN A SEMITONE

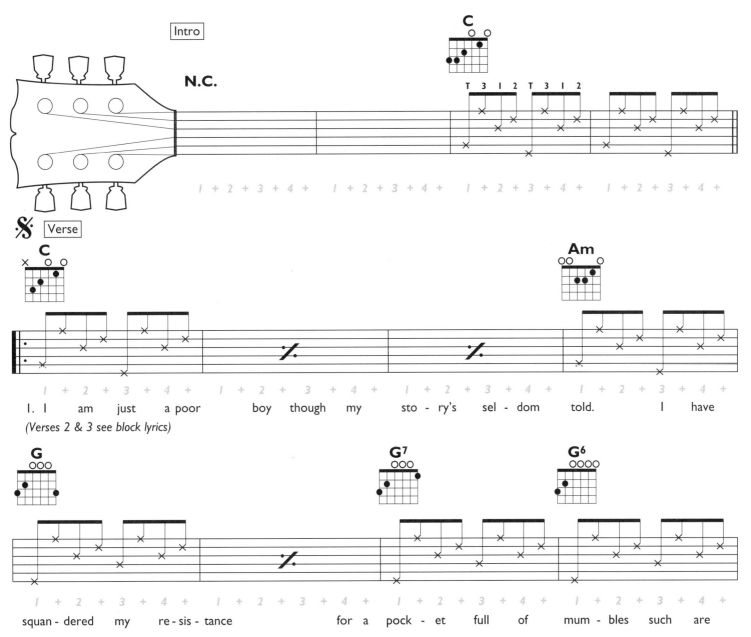

1. I am just a poor boy though my sto - ry's sel - dom told.   I have

(Verses 2 & 3 see block lyrics)

squan - dered my re - sis - tance   for a pock - et full of mum - bles such are

57

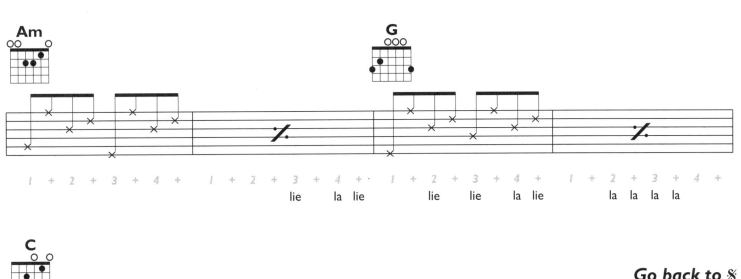

lie   la lie   lie   lie   la lie   la la la la

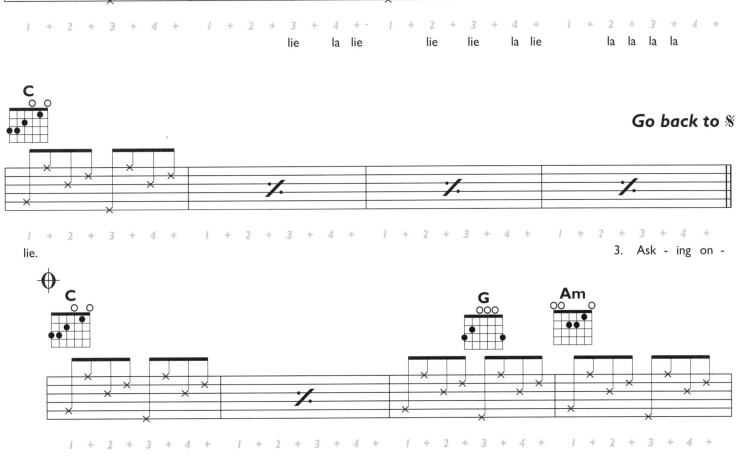

Go back to 𝄋

lie.   3.   Ask - ing on -

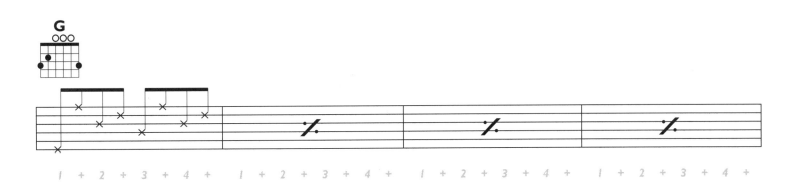

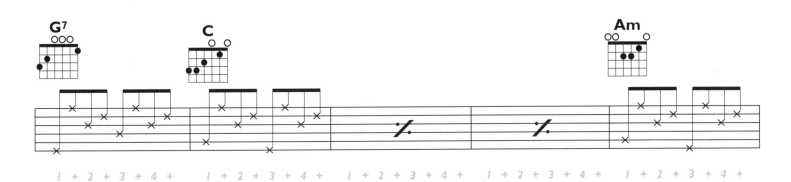

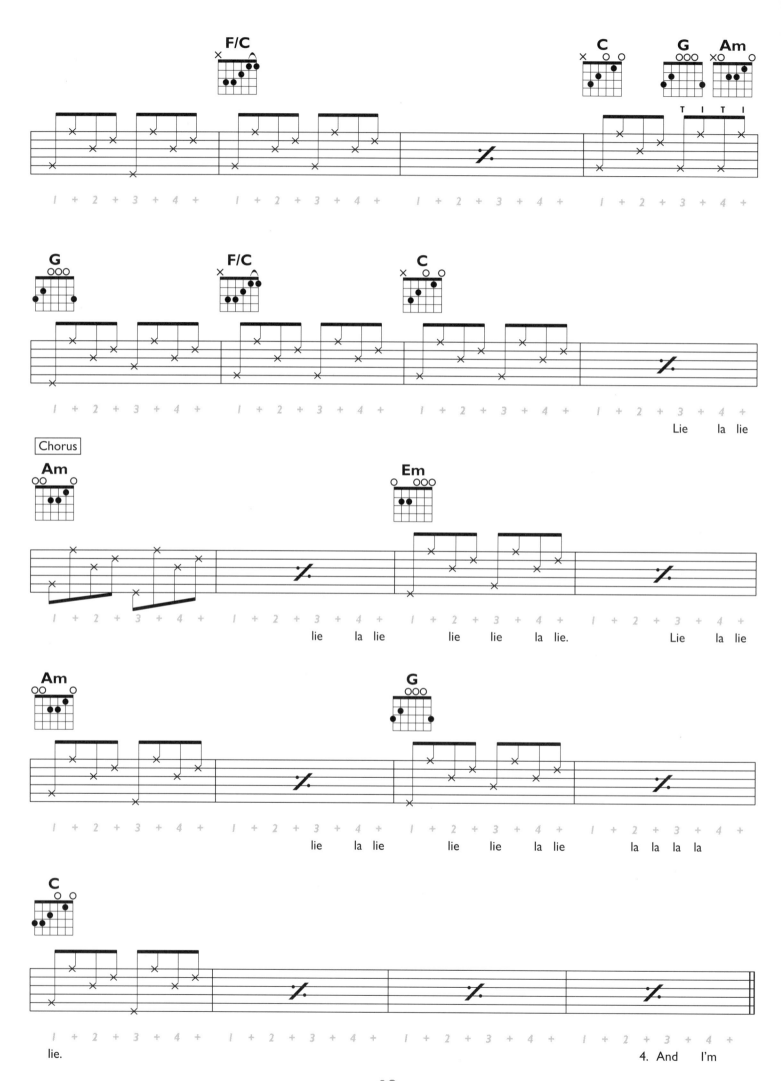

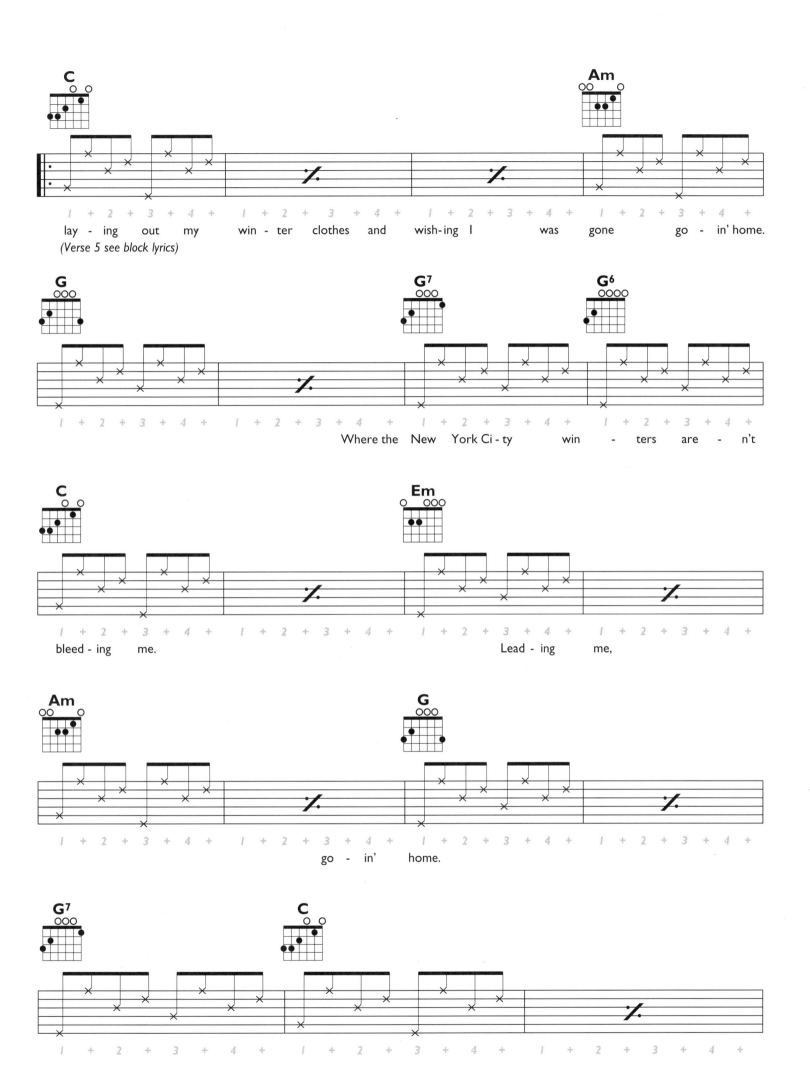

lay - ing out my win - ter clothes and wish-ing I was gone go - in' home.
(Verse 5 see block lyrics)

Where the New York Ci - ty win - ters are - n't

bleed - ing me.

Lead - ing me,

go - in' home.

1. **2.**

1 + 2 + 3 + 4 +   1 + 2 + 3 + 4 +   1 + 2 + 3 + 4 +

5. In the clear -   lie la

Chorus

Am   Em

1 + 2 + 3 + 4 +   1 + 2 + 3 + 4 +   1 + 2 + 3 + 4 +   1 + 2 + 3 + 4 +

lie.   Lie   lie lie   lie   lie   la lie.   Lie   la lie

Am   G

Play 8 times

1 + 2 + 3 + 4 +   1 + 2 + 3 + 4 +   1 + 2 + 3 + 4 +   1 + 2 + 3 + 4 +

lie   le lie   lie lie   la lie.

Outro

C   C   G   Am

1 + 2 + 3 + 4 +   1 + 2 + 3 + 4 +   1 + 2 + 3 + 4 +   1 + 2 + 3 + 4 +

G

1 + 2 + 3 + 4 +   1 + 2 + 3 + 4 +   1 + 2 + 3 + 4 +   1 + 2 + 3 + 4 +

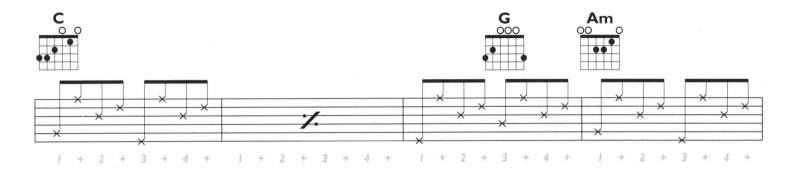

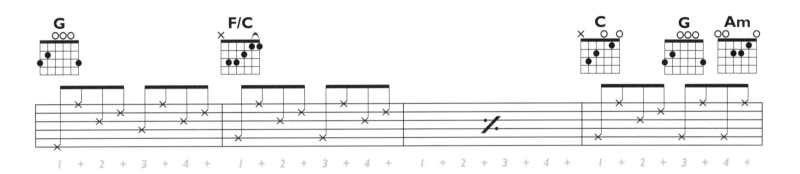

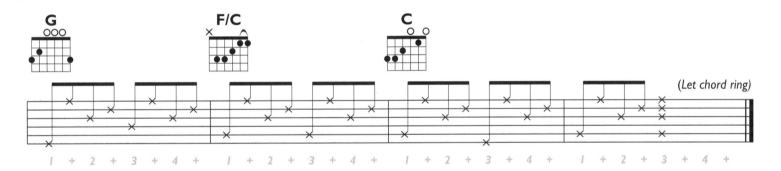

(Let chord ring)

Verse 2:
When I left my home
And my family,
I was no more than a boy,
In the company of strangers,
In the quiet of the railway station,
Running scared,
Laying low,
Seeking out the poorer quarters,
Where the ragged people go,
Looking for the places
Only they would know.

Verse 3:
Asking only workman's wages
I come looking for a job,
But I get no offers,
Just a come-on from the whores
On Seventh Avenue
I do declare,
There were times when I was so lonesome
I took some comfort there.

Verse 5:
In the clearing stands a boxer,
And a fighter by his trade
And he carries the reminders
Of ev'ry glove that laid him down
Or cut him till he cried out
In his anger and his shame,
"I am leaving, I am leaving."
But the fighter still remains.

1 2 3 4 5 6 7 8 9

EASY PICKINGS

Check out these other great titles...

EASY PICKINGS ACOUSTIC SONGS

JOLENE DOLLY PARTON
LOVE IS ALL AROUND THE TROGGS
IMAGINE JOHN LENNON
SONGBIRD EVA CASSIDY
FATHER AND SON CAT STEVENS
CALIFORNIA DREAMIN' THE MAMAS & THE PAPAS
GOOD PEOPLE JACK JOHNSON
A DESIGN FOR LIFE MANIC STREET PREACHERS
DRIFTWOOD TRAVIS
FIX YOU COLDPLAY
HALF THE WORLD AWAY OASIS
SULTANS OF SWING DIRE STRAITS
UNCHAINED MELODY THE RIGHTEOUS BROTHERS
YOU RAISE ME UP JOSH GROBAN
YOU GIVE ME SOMETHING JAMES MORRISON
HERE, THERE AND EVERYWHERE THE BEATLES

Order No. AM991760

EASY PICKINGS PAUL SIMON

SCARBOROUGH FAIR / CANTICLE
DUNCAN
MOTHER AND CHILD REUNION
THE SOUND OF SILENCE
A HAZY SHADE OF WINTER
TAKE ME TO THE MARDI GRAS
WEDNESDAY MORNING, 3 A.M.
GRACELAND
THE 59TH STREET BRIDGE SONG (FEELIN' GROOVY)
MRS. ROBINSON
HOMEWARD BOUND
50 WAYS TO LEAVE YOUR LOVER
THAT'S WHERE I BELONG
KATHY'S SONG
AMERICA
AMERICAN TUNE

Order No. PS11649

EASY PICKINGS DYLAN

BLOWIN' IN THE WIND
MR. TAMBOURINE MAN
LIKE A ROLLING STONE
THINGS HAVE CHANGED
ALL ALONG THE WATCHTOWER
BLIND WILLIE McTELL
I WANT YOU
BOOTS OF SPANISH LEATHER
FOREVER YOUNG
TANGLED UP IN BLUE
**YOU'RE GONNA MAKE ME LONESOME
   WHEN YOU GO**
DON'T THINK TWICE, IT'S ALL RIGHT
LAY LADY LAY
MOST OF THE TIME
NOT DARK YET
ONE TOO MANY MORNINGS
IT AIN'T ME BABE

Order No. AM991782

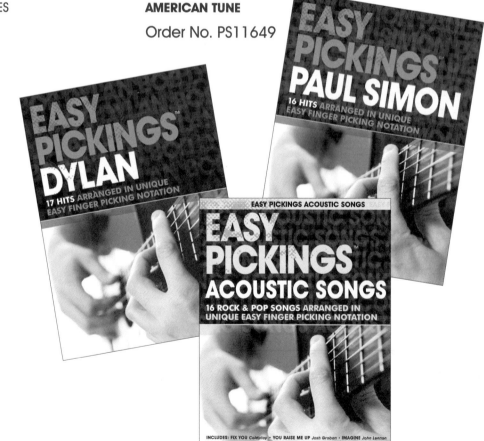

Visit your local music shop or, in case of difficulty, contact the Marketing Department,
Music Sales Limited, Newmarket Road, Bury St Edmunds, Suffolk IP33 3YB, UK.
www.musicsales.com